MIDDLE SCHOOLIN' IT

FIFTEEN SHORT PLAYS
FOR MIDDLE SCHOOL ACTORS

www.youthplays.com
info@youthplays.com
424-703-5315

TABLE OF CONTENTS

SNAKES IN A LUNCHBOX

A short dramedy by
Arthur M. Jolly

CAST OF CHARACTERS

CARLY, a mousy girl, ready to finally strike back.

GEORGIA, her quirky best friend.

PEYTON, a bully dealing with personal issues. Physically imposing over the other two. Female, but could also be male.

PLACE

The playing field behind a Florida middle school.

TIME

The present.

(GEORGIA carefully puts an old fashioned lunchbox on the ground. CARLY enters.)

CARLY: Did you get it?

GEORGIA: It's in there.

CARLY: Sweet! Can I see?

GEORGIA: No.

CARLY: Why not?

GEORGIA: It bites, and if it bit you, you would die, and then I'd have to tell your mom you're all dead, and your mom scares the cheese whiz out of me.

CARLY: How did you catch it?

GEORGIA: It was basking on a rock. I put the box down, and chased it in with a broom.

CARLY: That was incredibly brave.

GEORGIA: I am an incredibly brave girl.

CARLY: I owe you.

GEORGIA: You do. You owe me huge. Like, if I'm dying and I need a kidney, you gotta give me one of yours.

CARLY: I will give you both of them. And my liver.

GEORGIA: Why would I need a liver?

CARLY: Why would you need a kidney?

GEORGIA: Maybe I got bitten by a coral snake and my kidney exploded.

CARLY: That's what it does?

GEORGIA: I don't know. Google said they were the most poisonous snake in all of North America.

CARLY: Do you think it will hurt?

GEORGIA: Donating a kidney?

CARLY: Peyton Jean Charles. Getting bit. Will it hurt her?

GEORGIA: You mean, if the plan works.

CARLY: The plan will work.

GEORGIA: Google didn't say. *(Beat.)* But I don't think that dying from a bite of the most poisonous snake in North America could possibly — even a little bit — *not* hurt more than anything. In fact if you ask me, I think it'd be like getting hit by a car on the inside.

(Beat.)

CARLY: Good.

(PEYTON enters.)

GEORGIA: Peyton!

(Carly spins.)

CARLY: Peyton.

PEYTON: Hey.

(A beat.)

CARLY: I...I brought it, so you don't have to hit me or anything. Just take it.

PEYTON: I'm not... *(Beat.)* I need to talk to you.

CARLY: You can just take it and go. It's in the box. Which you can keep.

PEYTON: I don't want your lunch.

CARLY: Yesterday, you said —

PEYTON: Yesterday...I'm sorry, okay?

CARLY: What?

PEYTON: I apologize. I'm sorry I hit you. I'm sorry I pulled your hair. And I'm sorry I called you a...I'm sorry for what I said.

(A pause.)

GEORGIA: Oh my gosh, her mom called you!

PEYTON: Her mom never —

GEORGIA: Hey, it's cool, I'm with you. Scary woman.

CARLY: *(To Georgia:)* Really?

GEORGIA: *(To Carly:)* I know you probably like her, but — oh yeah. I think it's her eyebrows.

PEYTON: Her mom didn't call me.

GEORGIA: *(Still to Carly:)* Most people have two of them. The Frida Kahlo thing — yeesh.

PEYTON: Who's Frida Kahlo?

CARLY: So why would you —

PEYTON: *(To Carly:)* Is she always like this?

CARLY: You get used to it.

PEYTON: Okay. Anyway, I'm sorry. So. That's it.

(Peyton turns to leave.)

CARLY: That's it?

PEYTON: It's over.

CARLY: You have been tormenting me —

PEYTON: Tormenting?

CARLY: —Since the fourth grade. You are the most...you are my nemesis.

PEYTON: I don't know what that is.

CARLY: You're a bully, Peyton. You have... *(Beat.)* Didn't you know? *(Beat.)* There are kids in this school who go to bed crying because they have to deal with you, because you're...because they know that the next morning, their mom's gonna drop them off in front of the school, and the moment they are out of sight of the car, there's nothing safe for them, there's nowhere they can go in the whole school that you and your evil, stupid, hateful gang of friends might not just be...just turn up, and hurt them or make them feel small and...and trapped. Nowhere safe. Do you have any idea what that's like? *(Beat.)* You're sorry? Now, you're sorry?

PEYTON: I'm...things are different. They just...I can't help it if my friends...I'm not gonna be like that. Not anymore. So, keep your lunch. And I'm sorry.

(Peyton starts to leave.)

GEORGIA: What happened?

PEYTON: I don't have to tell you —

GEORGIA: Well, no. But you might want to.

PEYTON: What?

GEORGIA: It sounds like you're about to lose the undying admiration of the gang of hate...which means, unless my math is off, you're gonna be out of friends in this place — not that I'm offering...but who else are you gonna tell? *(Beat.)* What happened?

(A pause.)

PEYTON: Last night, my dad left the halfway house, came over and punched my mom in the face a bunch until she picked up a knife out of the sink and stuck it in his arm. Which is...he's okay. I mean, he's not dead or anything, but the way she looked when...he's gonna be in the hospital for a bit 'cause she hit an artery, and then he's going back inside. It's a violation of his condition of release or something, so there isn't even going to be a trial or nothing. The thing is...when she did it, I wasn't...I saw them fight, you know, before he — I mean, the first time. They fought a bunch, but she never...it was always them fighting. The two of them, it's how they were. Last night, I looked at her face — and I thought she was going to kill him. Stab him in the neck, or the heart. And I didn't feel bad about it. Not one bit. I just thought: took you long enough, Momma. *(Beat.)* Don't tell anyone. *(Beat.)* Never mind, say whatever. I figure everyone will know in a day or two anyway. They always do.

GEORGIA: Maybe. But they won't hear it from us.

PEYTON: Thanks. *(Beat.)* Cool lunchbox. Very retro.

(Peyton exits.)

GEORGIA: That was not what I was expecting.

CARLY: I don't...it's not fair.

GEORGIA: What part?

CARLY: Any part. Three years, and I—what? Have to just forgive her because her dad's a psycho criminal who stabbed her mom?

GEORGIA: Other way round.

CARLY: No! I have a snake in a lunchbox! I have the most poisonous snake in all of North America waiting—in a lunchbox! The ultimate revenge, the best turn-around revenge ever in the history of ever...

GEORGIA: Her mom stabbed her dad with a knife, you gotta—

CARLY: Why? Why do I have to, what—forgive her for everything?

(A beat.)

GEORGIA: Do you think they're gonna keep the knife? I mean, could you ever use it again?

CARLY: She just...ruined it. She ruined my whole plan.

GEORGIA: It'd be so weird—you'd be like, cutting a steak, and thinking—that's the one that was in Dad's arm. That's just gross. Then again, my mom used a knife to dig a bunch of hair and stuff out of the drain the other week, and we still use that one...

CARLY: I hate her. I think I hate her more now.

GEORGIA: She did wash it.

CARLY: This sucks.

(A pause.)

GEORGIA: The thing is...you didn't get your revenge on Peyton. But if the plan was to stop her bullying you... *(She shrugs:)* Right?

CARLY: I guess so.

GEORGIA: We do still have a problem.

(They look at the lunch box.)

CARLY: D'you think it'll be angry?

GEORGIA: After being swept into a lunchbox and then stuck there all morning?

CARLY: So...yes.

GEORGIA: I'd think so, yeah. Unless it's asleep.

CARLY: It might be asleep.

GEORGIA: Here's my plan. We open the box very, very quietly — and then we run away.

CARLY: It's not a very good plan.

GEORGIA: Neither was yours.

CARLY: What if we just took the box with the snake still in it and threw the whole thing —

GEORGIA: No. I said in the beginning, we don't hurt the snake. I support PETA.

CARLY: You were okay with Peyton getting —

GEORGIA: They don't have an organization for the ethical treatment of Peyton.

CARLY: True. *(Beat.)* Shall we?

(A pause.)

GEORGIA: I'm trying to find a reason to say no. Nope. Don't have one.

CARLY: Quietly.

GEORGIA: Very quietly.

(They slowly, slowly, creep up on the box. Unlatch it achingly carefully...Carly reaches out with one foot and flips the lid open. They look.)

CARLY: It's empty.

GEORGIA: Yeah.

CARLY: So, the coral snake...

GEORGIA: Crawled out through that rusted hole in the corner and escaped.

CARLY: Oh.

(They become utterly paranoid from here on out.)

GEORGIA: This wasn't actually a very good plan at all.

CARLY: No. It really wasn't. Where did you keep the box?

GEORGIA: My locker.

CARLY: So the snake...

GEORGIA: Could be anywhere in the entire school by now.

CARLY: So there's...nowhere safe.

GEORGIA: Nope.

CARLY: Not even a little bit of a good plan.

GEORGIA: We're gonna have to tell someone. Everyone.

CARLY: We are gonna get in so much trouble.

(As they tiptoe, very gingerly, off.)

GEORGIA: On the plus side, when this gets out I don't think anyone is ever going to even consider beating you up for your lunch again.

CARLY: So let's say the plan half worked.

GEORGIA: I wish I had a broom.

    (They exit. Blackout. End of play.)

The Author Speaks

Was the structure of the play influenced by any other work?
I don't think so—this one flowed very organically. I didn't even know what was going to happen when Peyton enters. The first line I gave her was "I'm sorry." I remember sitting there for a minute, wondering what would happen if a bully had a change of heart offstage, not during the scene, not as part of the story. I was worried I was shooting myself in the foot by missing the dramatic moment when she changed from bully to friend—or at least, into a decent person—but eventually I thought: Well, see where it goes. A couple of pages later and I knew that it was the right choice—it's not Peyton's story, it's Carly's. What happens when a perfect revenge plan gets derailed because the victim no longer deserves it? Or does that even matter?

Have you dealt with the same theme in other works that you have written?
There are some similar themes in *Long Joan Silver*— explorations of what makes good people do bad things and vice versa...and in some ways, every one of my plays is about the shifting power dynamics between characters...but then, isn't every play?

What writers have had the most profound effect on your style?
A friend of mine, Stephen Rajkumar (probably the funniest person I've ever known), gave me one of the most useful pieces of advice, years and years ago. I was telling him a great idea for a script, and going into all the funny moments, and he looked at me and said "Just shut up! Shut up and write it." He knew that I was all talk back then—that I was happy to come up with ideas and pipe dreams and scenarios, but that I wasn't doing anything concrete to put them down on paper. He was absolutely right, and to this day I have a piece of paper over my desk that says: Shut up and write it.

What do you hope to achieve with this work?
Peace on earth and the perfect recipe for a chocolate chip cookie. If one or two people examine and re-evaluate their bullying behavior, or their response to others who bully, that would be nice too.

What are the most common mistakes that occur in productions of your work?
Actors miss the meaning of punctuation. It's fairly uniform for modern playwrights, and it changes the meaning of the lines. An ellipsis (...) means an actor trails off, they stop talking. A hyphen or em-dash (—) means they are interrupted. Acting is about finding choices—but you need to start from a place of understanding what the text reveals. An ellipsis means a character has *made a choice* not to say something; a dash means a character has been *stopped* from achieving their goal of saying those words—that difference changes the character.

What inspired you to become a playwright?
My first production, at the Summer Shorts Festival at the Miami City Theatre. I saw a notice online that they were accepting ten minute plays. I'd been writing for years, but I'd never even considered writing a play. I saw the notice and thought "Ten minutes? I could write a *ten minute* play." I did, it was accepted from over 850 submissions, and a couple of months later, I was watching my first ever play on stage in front of an audience of 300, sandwiched in between Paul Rudnick's **Pride & Joy** and Colin Mitchell's **The Leap**. Feeling the audience response all around me clarified what I wanted to do in my writing and in my life. I've been writing plays ever since.

How did you research the subject?
I actually started out wanting to be a herpetologist and study snakes. At one point, I had twenty-seven of them in various tanks in a New York apartment. I worked in the reptile house of Jersey Zoo and at the Herpetological Lab at NYU as a teenager...and then I moved into other interests as I grew

older. The only trouble is that the moment I decided it was a snake in the lunchbox, I threw all that knowledge out because I didn't actually care. Coral snakes might technically be the most poisonous snake in North America because of their particular type of venom, but they are very timid and rarely bite. They also have tiny fangs—you have to work to get bitten by a coral snake. That's not a suggestion, of course. The whole "don't try this at home" warning was specifically written about harassing poisonous snakes and putting them in lunchboxes—only later did it spread to science experiments, fireworks, stock car racing, etc. You're also not going to find one basking on a rock; you'd have to dig for them under rotting logs. Brooms are not involved at all.

Are any characters modeled after real life or historical figures?
There might be a little in Peyton's character of a boy I knew in primary school in the UK. He was the quintessential "school bully," with a charming reputation as an abuser of animals to boot... It's only looking back as an adult that I realize he must've had a horrific family life. People who feel the need to hurt others—especially animals—are almost always acting as a way to try and find an outlet for their own pain.

Shakespeare gave advice to the players in *Hamlet*; if you could give advice to your cast what would it be?
Take your time, have fun, and give the audience permission to laugh. Let them finish before jumping in with the next line, even if you're sure that's the line that'll get a bigger laugh—comedy is about timing; and it's more often rushed than played too slowly. Find the funny...there are many, many more jokes than the ones in the text. A look, a reaction can add a whole new laugh—find those moments in rehearsal. There are also some very powerful, dramatic moments, and not only in Peyton's monologue. Speaking of her monologue, though, be ready for the audience to start out laughing—they may not catch on that things have taken a turn for the dark

immediately. Be patient with them. When they get there, they will also be dealing with their own emotional experience of having just laughed at something brutally real and painful, and that can give the moment even more impact. Trust in the scene and your acting.

About the Author

Arthur M. Jolly was recognized by the Academy of Motion Picture Arts and Sciences with a Nicholl Fellowship in Screenwriting, and is the playwright of *A Gulag Mouse* (Finalist Woodward/Newman Drama Award, Winner Off-Broadway Competition, Joining Sword and Pen Competition), *A Very Modern Marriage* (Semi-Finalist Eugene O'Neill Theatre Center Playwrights Conference), *Past Curfew* (AOPW Fellowship winner), *Trash* (Semi-Finalist Eugene O'Neill Theatre Center Playwrights Conference) and a collection of ten-minute plays, *Guilty Moments*. Other YouthPLAYS titles include *Long Joan Silver*, *The Christmas Princess*, *What the Well Dressed Girl is Wearing* and *How Blue is My Crocodile*. Jolly is a member of WGA, DGA, ALAP and is represented by the Brant Rose Agency.

PIGLET

A short comedy by
Brian Armstrong

CAST OF CHARACTERS

PIGLET, a pig, prince of the Barnyard.

FELINIA, a cat, daughter of Ponius.

COWDIUS, a cow, Piglet's uncle, engaged to Goatrude.

GOATRUDE, a goat, Piglet's mother, queen of the Barnyard.

PONIUS, parent of Felinia, member of the royal court.

GHOST, the ghost of Piglet's father, the old King Ham.

SETTING

The barnyard of a small farm.

PRODUCTION NOTES

The character of Ponius is written as female, but can easily be made into a male character as needed simply by changing pronouns and the word "mother" into "father." The character has been done both ways in the past. If a larger cast is needed to give more students participation, any other farm animals can be added in non-speaking roles.

The animal nature of the costumes can be quite literal or simply hinted at. In previous productions this has been done with half-masks and with stage make-up or face paint.

SCENE 1

(PIGLET is sleeping peacefully in his pigsty. The GHOST of his Father, the old King Ham, drifts in behind him.)

GHOST: Piiigleeeet...Piiiigleeeet...

(No response. Ghost swiftly kicks Piglet then resumes a ghostly pose.)

Hey, wake up you lazy sow.

PIGLET: Huh? What? Whozzere?

(Piglet turns to see the Ghost and screams.)

GHOST: Piglet...I am your father...

PIGLET: But, but, you're dead. The farmer took you and made you into breakfast.

GHOST: No! I was murdered by your Uncle Cowdius. He poisoned me in my slop, then when I pigged out (as usual), I died. *Then* the farmer made me into breakfast.

PIGLET: But then, wouldn't the poison have killed the farmer and his wife when they ate you?

GHOST: No, but I did give them teeerrrible gaaas. Teeeribllee...

PIGLET: Ugghh...I shouldn't have eaten that rotten fruit...it always gives me crazy dreams.

GHOST: This is no dream. Cowdius killed me so that he could marry your mother and become King of the Barnyard. You must avenge me and take your rightful place as king. Avenge me, Piglet. Aveeenge meee.

PIGLET: What? No, that can't be true. Mom wouldn't marry Uncle Cowdius. That's just gross.

GHOST: You'll see. You'll see...

(Ghost fades away [exits].)

PIGLET: That was weird. Now, for some reason, I'm *(Yawns:)* very sleepy.

(Piglet lays down to sleep. Enter GOATRUDE.)

GOATRUDE: PIIIGLEEEET!!! Get up and get dressed! You are not going to be late to my wedding!

PIGLET: Wedding?

GOATRUDE: Yes, wedding! Don't tell me you forgot that today's the day I'm marrying Cowdius.

PIGLET: You're what?

(The Ghost pops up briefly behind Piglet.)

GHOST: I tooold you so...

(Ghost exits.)

GOATRUDE: What was that?

PIGLET: Dad...

GOATRUDE: Your father is gone, and nothing is going to bring him back. You don't expect your dear old mom to be alone and miserable forever, do you?

PIGLET: It's only been a week!

GOATRUDE: Oh, don't exaggerate. Now I'm sure I told Cowdius to break the news to you. I remember because it was just after he bought me this gorgeous ring. Isn't it fabulous?

PIGLET: Mom, wait—I had this crazy dream last night and—

GOATRUDE: —Uh-huh, that's nice dear. Now clean yourself up, I want you looking handsome this evening. And clean your room while you're at it. It's a pigsty.

(Exit Goatrude. Piglet starts cleaning.)

SCENE 2

(Enter FELINIA.)

FELINIA: Piglet! Hi...are you excited or what? Isn't this soo cool, a royal wedding. Giving you any ideas?

PIGLET: Not now, Felinia. Geez, my dad hasn't been buried a fortnight and already a wedding? This is crazy.

FELINIA: I know, right, like your mother gets another wedding already? Isn't it someone else's turn?

PIGLET: *(Not really listening:)* I've got to find out the truth...

FELINIA: Maybe I'll catch the bouquet tonight... Oh! Tonight! Piglet, I need your help, that's why I came here.

PIGLET: What does Cowdius want?

FELINIA: Exactly! He asked me to take care of the entertainment for tonight, but I don't know what to do. He doesn't seem to like anything. Maybe some jugglers, or a play or —

PIGLET: That's it! A play!

FELINIA: Really; you like my idea? Okay, we'll do a play, and my mom can be in it; she's a really good actress and...

PIGLET: Yes, the play's the thing, by which I'll catch the conscience of the king. Go bring your mother. We've got to rehearse.

(Felinia exits.)

PIGLET: When the actors take the stage, they'll enact a horrendous murder, a king poisoned by his brother. If Cowdius did indeed kill my father, it will show on his lying face when he sees his treachery on stage.

(Felinia returns with PONIUS.)

PONIUS: Piglet, there you are. I'm so excited. Felinia tells me you're going to help us with our play. I used to be quite the actor in my day you know. Why your father never missed a performance, rest his soul.

PIGLET: Uh, right. So here's the plan.

(They get into a huddle and whisper. They exit.)

SCENE 3

(Enter COWDIUS and Goatrude.)

COWDIUS: Alright, alright, let's get on with this so I can hurry up and become king, uh, I mean, marry the most wonderful goat I've ever laid eyes on.

GOATRUDE: Oh, Cowdius, you're such a charmer. This is going to be wonderful. I hear my son helped out with the entertainment.

COWDIUS: Really? I didn't expect him to be so supportive.

GOATRUDE: Whyever not?

COWDIUS: You know, the whole taking his father's place thing, the fact that he'd be king if not for me marrying you, that old chestnut.

GOATRUDE: Never mind. I'm sure all Piglet wants is to see me happy. Oh, here they come.

PIGLET: Hear ye, hear ye. For the entertainment of his majesty, and her majesty, and uh, my majesty, the royal court has planned some fine entertainment. We thought you might appreciate a little, dinner theatre. Tonight we present: Regicide—a Murder Mystery.

(Cowdius looks nervous.)

GOATRUDE: Oh, how exciting. Don't you think so, dear?

COWDIUS: Yes, exciting.

PIGLET: In this scene, the king is getting ready for his daily slop. Meanwhile, a foul plot is afoot...

(Piglet sets up the slop in the pig pen.)

I am the king's servant, preparing his meal.

(Enter Felinia.)

FELINIA: Take a hike. I'll make it worth your while.

COWDIUS: Bribing the servants, how foul.

GOATRUDE: Hush.

(Piglet takes the bribe and exits the "stage" but stays on the side to watch Cowdius.)

FELINIA: Now, where did I put that poison? Ah here it is!

(Felinia poisons the slop with a large bottle of poison.)

COWDIUS: Come on; who uses that much poison—or any at all?

(Goatrude shushes him.)

PIGLET: Hmm, I think he protests too much!

(Ponius enters, overacting.)

PONIUS: Oh, I have such a mighty royal hunger. I can't wait to pig out!

(Ponius puts her face down into the feeding trough and then hams up a death scene.)

COWDIUS: What? I won't stand for these lies. It didn't happen like that! I mean, nothing happened. The entertainment is over. Where's the clergyman? Let's get this wedding finished.

GOATRUDE: He won't be here for another hour, dear.

COWDIUS: Who needs him? By the power invested in me as rightful heir to the throne, I hereby pronounce us married. Long live the king! Let's go, Goatrude.

GOATRUDE: Oh, how spontaneous!

(As they exit, Piglet calls after Cowdius.)

PIGLET: You fiend! You killed my father! You shall pay for this!

PONIUS: I don't understand? Didn't they like our play? But I was so great in it! Your majesties, wait!

(She exits.)

FELINIA: Well, it seems a shame to waste all this wedding preparation. What do you think, Piglet—shall we take the next step in our relationship?

PIGLET: What relationship? What are you talking about, you crazy cat? Let me be! Get thee to a hennery!

FELINIA: Crazy!? I'll show you crazy! Nobody dumps Felinia!

(Felinia goes crazy, throwing things around, and ultimately drowns in the slop.)

PIGLET: Oh great, now Felinia's dead. Is dying the latest fashion trend now? Why, just before Dad was killed, my best friend was eaten by the farmer and his wife. All they left were scraps. Why, there's a piece over there.

(He picks up a pork chop or other pork product.)

Oh, Porkatio, I knew you well. Perhaps I should join you. Life is just too much to bear. I should just march up to that farmer and say "Hey, breakfast!" To be bacon, or not to be bacon, that is the question.

(He tosses aside the pork chop.)

No! I will avenge my father's death! I will kill Cowdius!

(Piglet exits.)

SCENE 4

(Goatrude enters followed by Ponius.)

PONIUS: Are you sure you're not upset about the play?

GOATRUDE: Oh, it's fine dear, don't worry yourself about it. Actually I rather enjoyed it.

PONIUS: Yes, I was rather good wasn't I?

GOATRUDE: Yes, I don't know why Cowdius hated it so.

PONIUS: Hated?

GOATRUDE: Yes, he said he would behead the person responsible, but I'm sure he was exaggerating. He'll be here any minute. Why don't you ask him?

PONIUS: Here? Oh no, I've got to hide!

(Ponius hides, Piglet comes along, sneaking, trying to spy on his mother.)

GOATRUDE: Don't be silly, stop hiding. It's not like he's actually going to kill you.

PIGLET: *(To audience:)* Ah ha! She must be hiding Cowdius. He knows I'm coming for him! There's no other possible explanation!

(Piglet jumps out and kills Ponius, hiding behind the hay.)

GOATRUDE: Ah! You killed her! Piglet, why would you do such a thing?

PIGLET: Uhh...oops?

GOATRUDE: Oops? Oops!?! You killed a member of the royal court and my good friend for no reason and all you can say is "oops"? My son is a murderer! I don't want to live in this world! Give me that!

(Goatrude takes Piglet's sword and stabs herself.)

PIGLET: Cowdius! Where are you? Show yourself!

(Cowdius enters holding a sword.)

COWDIUS: Ah, Piglet. You've killed your mother. Excellent. That'll save me some time. So, did you want something?

PIGLET: Hello, my name is Piglet Montoya, you killed my father, prepare to die!

COWDIUS: What? Never mind—on guard!

(They duel with their swords, Cowdius slices Piglet's arm, then Piglet runs Cowdius through with his sword.)

Ha! You fool—I poisoned the tip of my sword. You're as dead as I am! Ha hah ha—

(He dies.)

PIGLET: Oh, death! I am ready for thee...I shall make...delicious bacon...see you soon, Dad.

(Enter Ghost.)

GHOST: Well, now that we're all dead, I won't be so lonely, and I can once again be King of the Barnyard! Come out, everyone, and enjoy my ghostly kingdom!

(Everyone enters, takes a bow. Blackout. End of play.)

The Author Speaks

What inspired you to write this play?
I was teaching theatre to my middle school students and wanted to create a play that would be as fun for adults to watch as it is for students to perform. I had a small drama club at the time, and all of the plays I found that were age appropriate and that the students took an interest in had huge casts, intended for a full class play. Since I only had a few actors, I decided to write a short piece with them in mind. I thought immediately of Shakespeare and how his stories have laid the groundwork for so many inspired works. The idea then stuck me out of the blue to do *Hamlet* with animals, and *Piglet* was born. I researched all over the internet to see if anyone had already done this idea, and fortunately, no one had.

Was the structure of the play influenced by any other work?
The basic plot structure was influenced by Shakespeare's *Hamlet*. I carefully chose key moments to highlight, as I knew a ten-minute play could only be a parody of *Hamlet*, not a representation. From there I tried to simply have fun with it, play with the language and make myself laugh. Then I tested it with my students to see if they would enjoy it and they did.

What writers have had the most profound effect on your style?
So many writers have influenced me over the years, though the influence may not be blatantly present in this particular work. One of my all-time favorite authors is F. Scott Fitzgerald, who writes such beautiful, poetic prose, and I try to be as whimsical with language as he is. I also am inspired by such sci-fi and fantasy writers as Douglas Adams and Terry Pratchett, who bring out the kid in me. I love the absurdist playwrights such as Eugene Ionesco and his *The Lesson*, as

well as Samuel Beckett. Luigi Pirandello I consider to be a great pioneer in pushing the envelope of what theatre can be. Finally, my greatest inspiration as a playwright is my former professor Tom Smith, who has written many great comedies and adaptations which have been produced around the world.

What were the biggest challenges involved in the writing of this play?

The greatest challenge was adapting the play for production in any kind of school, whatever facilities and budget (or lack of) may be available. The first time this was performed, the school had just begun a drama program and had essentially no budget, but we managed to make it work and put on a good show.

What are the most common mistakes that occur in productions of your work?

In the scene of the "play within a play," there is some set change that needs to be practiced extensively to make sure it occurs seamlessly. This can be helped by having stage hands dressed as animals so that they blend into the world of the play, or by having the characters Piglet, Felinia, and Ponius move the set pieces as necessary.

Also, as the characters "die," there is the issue of what to do with the bodies. Felinia, for example, goes unnoticed until the end, so Piglet can either cover her with something, or if possible, roll her off stage onto a padded area.

I would also recommend that if this is done at a school, it would be best to dual cast the play if there are enough actors, that way rather than having "understudies," you have two full casts that will get the chance to perform for an audience.

What inspired you to become a playwright?
I have been inspired to write and act as long as I can remember, but it was a dedicated college professor that encouraged and supported me, giving me the inspiration to seriously peruse playwriting. I had woken up in the night with an idea fully formed for a script and though I had no idea of proper formatting at the time, I wrote out a draft by hand in two days, and typed an edited version the week after. I asked a professor I had only had a few acting classes with to look it over, as I knew he taught playwriting as well. He read it in one day and spent an hour with me talking over the play and encouraging me to peruse my potential. The first time one of my plays was produced, I had not been a part of the rehearsal process. When I saw the characters from my mind in the flesh on the stage, it was the most incredible feeling, like creating life. This feeling keeps me coming back to playwriting.

Are any characters modeled after real life or historical figures?
No. The characters are essentially parodies and amalgamations of the characters in *Hamlet*, along with a healthy dose of imagination and inspiration drawn from the animal natures they represent. I wrote them with middle school kids in mind, so the personalities reflect that. I then named the characters after characters in the Shakespeare play, in many cases combining several characters into one. Hamlet became Piglet, Ophelia became Felinia, Claudius-Cowdius, Gertrude-Goatrude and Polonius-Ponius. Porkatio is taken from Horatio, but is a combination including Yorick, Rosencrantz and Guildenstern.

Shakespeare gave advice to the players in *Hamlet*; if you could give advice to your cast what would it be?
Make big choices and try to have fun with it. Make sure to work together as a cast, as a team, and help each other

through the difficult moments in both rehearsal and performance. Most of all, don't panic. If you perform with confidence, even through the mistakes, the audience will not realize that anything is wrong. Once you have the lines memorized and are comfortable with it, try a super-fast run through, then an over-the-top run-through to get you inspired for the final performance.

About the Author

Brian Armstrong is a writer, a teacher, and a proud father. He received his MA in Script Writing from The Royal Central School of Speech and Drama in London and has had several plays produced for the stage in the US and England. Brian has also published a book of poetry. He is a member of the Old Pueblo Playwrights in Tucson, Arizona.

MY BIG ADELE MOMENT

A short dramedy by
Kenyon Brown

CAST OF CHARACTERS

LIV, female, age 13, any race. Competitive. A lot of attitude.

SARA, female, age 13, any race. Smart, less sophisticated.

SETTING

Backstage at a middle school auditorium. Evening dress rehearsal for a talent show.

TIME

The present.

SUGGESTED PROPS

A microphone ("mic").

PRODUCTION NOTES

This play is intended for middle school and high school students. It might not be appropriate for younger audiences. The following songs are referred to in the play: "Rolling in the Deep," "Chasing Pavements" and "Set Fire to the Rain" (Adele); "Stronger" (Kelly Clarkson), and "I Knew You Were Trouble" (Taylor Swift). With the exception of the Adele songs, the songs can be changed to suit the production. The names of the television reality shows mentioned in the play can be updated if necessary.

(Backstage at a middle school auditorium. Evening. LIV is holding a mic, mouthing the words to a song, swaying in place. SARA is sitting in a chair, watching, listening.)

SARA: Wait! That is wrong!

LIV: What?

SARA: Olivia, why is Chantal singing now? Jordan's supposed to be singing.

(She looks at the rehearsal schedule. Liv suddenly stops, listens.)

LIV: Mrs. Merritt changed the order.

SARA: Why'd she do that?

LIV: It's good she's switched the lineup. OMG, as if Chantal can even sing.

SARA: Since when is Chantal singing "Stronger"?

LIV: Sara, who cares? If you're not singing Adele, why bother singing?

SARA: But I thought Chantal was singing "Chasing Pavements."

LIV: Pul-ease! No way can she sing Adele. Somebody had to tell her. It would be sooo embarrassing.

SARA: You told her she should sing a different song?

LIV: Well, yea-ahh. Something better suited to her voice. It definitely would never be my song choice. But Chantal doesn't have much range. So the song is fine for her.

SARA: Just because it's not an Adele song doesn't mean it's not good.

LIV: Chantal's definitely not an Adele girl. The sooner she gets it, the better.

SARA: There are a lot of other good singers is all I'm saying.

LIV: Stop the show! They don't bring it like Adele.

SARA: Chantal sounds pretty good.

LIV: You think so?

SARA: Really good.

LIV: She does sound good, doesn't she? I hate her!

(She continues mouthing words to a song.)

SARA: Olivia, what's with the mic?

LIV: My new vocal coach says it should be an extension of my hand.

SARA: Seriously?

LIV: She says I should carry it with me at all times. To help me prepare. "Set Fire to the Rain" is a hard song.

SARA: Wait, you're singing "Rolling in the Deep."

LIV: Stop the show! My mom spoke to Mrs. Merritt. She said it was okay for me to switch my song.

SARA: You changed your song just like that?

LIV: Sara, I'm not going to sing the same song you're singing.

SARA: We can both sing "Rolling in the Deep." It's the school talent show, not a competition.

LIV: "Set Fire to the Rain" is going to be totally epic.

SARA: Olivia, you think everything you sing is epic.

LIV: Because it is. And BTW, it's Liv now. Please stop calling me "Olivia."

SARA: Sor-ry. I've only called you Olivia since like forever. What's wrong with "Rolling in the Deep"?

LIV: Sara, people will think you're copying me.

SARA: Excuse me?

LIV: I'm just trying to help you.

SARA: I was the one who chose the song first, then you decided to sing it.

LIV: I don't think so.

SARA: You always copy me. Don't deny it. Ever since we were little. Like when I started collecting American Girl dolls. When I got Julie for my seventh birthday, you had to get Julie.

LIV: I got Julie first.

SARA: No, I did. Then when I got her best friend, Ivy, you couldn't wait until you got Ivy.

LIV: Since I had Julie, for sure I wanted to get Ivy.

SARA: Only because I got her first. You've been copying me ever since I can remember.

LIV: Sara, I don't play with dolls anymore.

SARA: But you're still copying me.

LIV: So why am I singing "Set Fire to the Rain" and you're not? Huh? My coach says it's better suited to my voice. And I need to show I have range. Like everyone sings "Rolling in the Deep."

SARA: It's a great song.

LIV: I want to be original.

SARA: Hel-lo-oo, you can't be original when you're singing an Adele song, Olivia. I mean, Liv.

LIV: I'm making it part of my repertoire.

SARA: Like since when do you have repertoire?

LIV: I need a repertoire for when I'm going to audition for *The X Factor*. If I make it, this agent my coach has been talking to will represent me.

SARA: *American Idol* is better.

LIV: It's sooo over. *The X Factor* is it.

SARA: What about *The Voice*?

LIV: Pul-lease. It's sooo cheesy. The judges make it all about themselves when it should be about the performers.

(Sara stops, listens. She looks at sheet of paper.)

SARA: Wait, Abby's singing now?

(Both girls listen.)

LIV: It's better all the weaker singers go first. Can you believe Abby's singing "I Knew You Were Trouble"? Ouch! The girl can't sing. She's really pitchy.

SARA: Abby sings good.

LIV: Not. Good is the enemy of great.

SARA: Huh?

LIV: If you're not great, you shouldn't be singing. That's what my coach says.

SARA: You don't think anyone can sing as good as you. You think everyone and every song are over. Except you and what you're singing. You probably think I'm over, too.

LIV: Sara, we're BFFs.

SARA: Yeah, right. Only when you feel like it. If I were Ivy, would you be Julie?

LIV: As if! Of course I would be Ivy. For a performer, Ivy is a totally cool name. It's Adele.

SARA: No, it's Ivy.

LIV: Exactly. I'd call myself just Ivy. Like Adele.

SARA: You always want what I have and make it yours.

LIV: You should be warming up, Sara. You don't want to sound pitchy.

SARA: Oh, now I'm pitchy?

LIV: I didn't say that. Never mind. Don't rehearse.

SARA: That's what this dress rehearsal is for.

LIV: Sara, you can never rehearse enough. Preparation is everything. It could be the moment.

SARA: What moment?

LIV: *The* moment.

SARA: You don't know what you're talking about.

LIV: You always have to be ready, Sara.

SARA: Well, I am ready.

LIV: You don't sound sure.

SARA: I'm sure, okay?

LIV: Every time you sing, you have to make it like it's real.

(*She stops, listens:*)

Oh, don't you just luuuvvv hearing Carter sing?

SARA: What's going on? Carter's not supposed to be singing now.

LIV: He's sooo cute. He could sing anything and I'd buy a ticket.

SARA: Mrs. Merritt has changed the order of everyone?

LIV: Finally we're hearing the stronger singers. Wouldn't it be totally epic if Carter and me sang a duet together? Or Randy. What about me and Randy singing a duet? He has a killer voice. I can't wait to hear Randy sing next.

SARA: Randy's singing next?

LIV: Our voices would sound sooo good together, don't you think? Randy sings as good as Carter. They're evenly matched.

SARA: How come you think the guys sing good, but not the girls?

LIV: Because they don't. FYI, there's nothing wrong with *The X Factor*.

SARA: I didn't say there was anything wrong with it.

LIV: You don't think I should audition?

SARA: I don't know.

LIV: Well, I am. It'll showcase my talent.

SARA: I wonder if "the X factor" is like a real thing.

LIV: *The X Factor* is a show, duh.

SARA: No, I mean like the Rh factor.

LIV: The what?

SARA: Rh factor. Rhesus factor. Blood.

LIV: Gross!

SARA: It's in your blood. You're going to need to know it for the science test tomorrow. Have you even studied for it?

LIV: Hel-loo. I've been rehearsing.

SARA: What's your blood type?

LIV: I don't know.

SARA: You're supposed to know it for the test. I'm O positive. Rh positive. Pretty common.

LIV: So you're the same as everybody else?

SARA: It's a common blood type.

LIV: I'm sure I'm not common.

SARA: That's not what I mean.

LIV: It's like that special something in your blood, the X factor. Either you have it or you don't.

SARA: Have what exactly?

LIV: It. Talent. The whole package.

SARA: Thank you for finally noticing.

LIV: I mean me.

SARA: You're the whole package? Yeah, right.

LIV: Sara, you don't even know how to sell it.

SARA: Sell what? What are you talking about?

LIV: You, your song. You gotta sell it, my coach says. With everything you're feeling. It's a performance. So perform.

SARA: I know that.

LIV: Why else do it unless you've giving like a 1000 percent, with everything you've got?

SARA: Since when are you like so professional?

LIV: You have to be it to do it. My coach says I could become a triple threat.

SARA: A what?

LIV: Triple threat. Don't you know anything? With training, I could sing, dance, and act.

SARA: Right...

LIV: She's helping me recreate myself. I can help you with your hair if you want.

SARA: I like my hair.

LIV: You do?

SARA: What's wrong with my hair?

LIV: Nothing.

SARA: My mom says you're wearing extensions.

LIV: Excuse me?

SARA: I guess on you, they work.

LIV: FYI, this is all my own hair.

SARA: Sure it is.

LIV: It is. My hair grows fast.

SARA: And it's more blonde.

LIV: I had it highlighted. Okay? To make it look natural. My mom does it for me. You should do it.

SARA: No way my mother will let me.

LIV: You're going to be in high school next year, Sara. You need your own look.

SARA: I do.

LIV: I don't think so. You look the same as everybody else. Your dress is nice. But it doesn't show you off.

SARA: What's wrong with my dress?

LIV: You can wear anything and you wear that dress? What's your style?

SARA: I don't know.

LIV: That's your problem. You need to know. You need a look that says, "This is me."

SARA: This is me.

LIV: Really? Stop the show!

(The girls listen.)

SARA: Wait, Jordan's singing…

SARA & LIV: *(Together:)* "Rolling in the Deep."

LIV: Jinx!

SARA: When did Jordan change her song?

LIV: Singing "Someone Like You" was definitely not the right Adele song for her.

SARA: You told her to sing "Rolling in the Deep"?

LIV: It was just a suggestion.

SARA: But I'm singing "Rolling in the Deep."

LIV: Yeah, so?

SARA: You were all set to sing "Rolling in the Deep" and then you changed to "Set Fire to the Rain" because I was singing "Rolling in the Deep." And then you told Jordan to sing it?

LIV: Jordan's version sounds decent, don't you think?

SARA: So it's not cool for you to sing "Rolling in the Deep," but it's cool for Jordan to sing it?

LIV: It is better suited to her voice. It has a stronger beat than "Someone Like You." A ballad is not right for her.

SARA: Who are you to say what the right song is for anyone?

LIV: I can have an opinion, can't I? At least Jordan works it. You can tell she's been rehearsing.

SARA: Olivia, you're unbelievable.

LIV: It's Liv. What? Sara, you can both sing the same song. It's not like you're competing. You even said so. You're a much better singer than Jordan. You don't have anything to worry about.

SARA: Why didn't you suggest another Adele song?

LIV: I thought it was a good choice for her. This rehearsal is taking like forever.

SARA: Out of all the Adele songs...

LIV: It was her decision.

SARA: Based on what you said.

LIV: What did I say?

SARA: She's singing my song, thank you very much.

LIV: Your song?

SARA: *(Shouting:)* YES, MY SONG!

LIV: Sara, chill.

SARA: Did you ever think about how I would feel?

LIV: Jordan's no competition if that's what you're concerned about. Believe me. You can outsing her any day of the week. All we do is keep stopping and starting the music. You'd think people would know their cues by now.

SARA: I just want this to be over.

LIV: Being a little nervous is good for your performance, Sara.

SARA: I'm not nervous.

LIV: It helps you focus on the show. Remember: all the training, all the rehearsing has prepared you for the big night. That's all you need to think about. Breathe. Deep steady breaths. You walk out on stage. The spotlight is on you. It's just you, the music, the song. Nothing else matters. I wonder if I have time to go to the restroom. Does my hair look good?

SARA: Oh, now my opinion matters.

LIV: Okay, I admit it. I got a spray tan, too. It helps my hair look more blonde.

SARA: Good for you.

LIV: You do what you have to do, Sara.

SARA: What is that supposed to mean?

LIV: You need an edge. You need to stand apart from the competition.

SARA: Why is everything a competition with you?

LIV: Because everything is. You don't earn a mansion with mediocrity.

SARA: Huh?

LIV: My coach says you'll never achieve your dreams if you don't push yourself. Aren't you excited? This is like beyond. Sara, I'm glad we're both singing Adele.

SARA: And now, because of you, Jordan is too.

LIV: What's the big deal?

SARA: You set me and her up to sing the same Adele song.

LIV: It's the school talent show. People are allowed to sing the same songs.

SARA: As long as nobody sings the same Adele song you're singing.

LIV: Then tell Jordan you don't want her to sing the same song.

SARA: Me tell Jordan?

LIV: Stop the show!

SARA: Stop saying that! It's totally annoying.

LIV: Just listen.

(The girls listen.)

With you two singing the same Adele song, people will hear

how you sing so much better than Jordan. I was only trying to help. I swear.

SARA: You think you're a way better singer than me, don't you?

LIV: No.

SARA: Yes. Admit it.

LIV: If you want me to tell Jordan to sing "Someone Like You," I will.

SARA: Just forget it.

LIV: I'll tell her I was wrong. Will that make you happy?

SARA: You're not a very good friend, O-liv-i-a.

LIV: Yes, I am.

SARA: Friends have each other's back.

LIV: Sara, don't be mad.

SARA: You just don't get it.

LIV: It's like destiny, you know?

SARA: What are you talking about?

LIV: Me and you. Singing Adele in the same show. We're both Adele girls, but we're different. It's good we're different.

SARA: Whatever.

LIV: You push me to sing better. Do I push you to sing better?

SARA: I guess.

LIV: You made the right song choice, Sara.

SARA: I'm so glad you think I was right about something.

LIV: My mom said "Rolling in the Deep" was more of a crowd pleaser. But I'm glad my coach talked her into letting me sing

"Set Fire to the Rain." It's a risk, but I have to take it. You sing "Rolling in the Deep" way better than me.

SARA: Really? You think so?

LIV: I was worried you'd sound better, okay?

SARA: You were? I had thought about singing "Set Fire to the Rain," but decided not to.

LIV: Yeah, right.

SARA: I did.

LIV: Sara, you don't have to be jealous of me.

SARA: I'm not. It is a hard song to sing. I tried, but I didn't sound good.

LIV: I hope I sing it well.

SARA: You will. You'll sound awesome. You always do.

LIV: Thank you. I really have to stand out. Don't you think you should get ready? You're on next.

SARA: Wait. You're on before I am.

LIV: Mrs. Merritt switched us. You're next. I'm singing last.

SARA: But the lineup always had me singing last.

LIV: My mom asked Mrs. Merritt if I could close the show.

SARA: It's Jordan, then me, then you?

LIV: Of course I'm the finale. It's going to be epic.

SARA: Why didn't you tell me?

LIV: The show always saves the best for last.

(Lights fade. End of play.)

The Author Speaks

What inspired you to write this play?

I was inspired by an actual middle school talent show that I attended. My niece performed a cello solo. Two of her friends sang different Adele songs. They were "big" songs for the girls to sing—and perhaps a little too ambitious. Both girls sang well, although one girl was more polished and the other girl was noticeably nervous; she forgot some of the words. Another friend of my niece's sang a Taylor Swift song. Later, my niece told me the girl who was nervous blamed the other girl who sang an Adele song. The girl who had chosen to sing the Taylor Swift song had wanted to sing an Adele song, but had been talked out of singing it by the girl who was more polished. All of this "backstage drama" got me thinking about friendships and competition, and how overly competitive friends can sometimes get.

Have you dealt with the same theme in other works that you have written?

I think most of my plays deal a little with competition between siblings or friends. However, I have never explored competition as fully as I do in *My Big Adele Moment*. What emerges from the play is how competitive friends can often become without realizing it, and how competition can test and hurt a friendship.

What writers have had the most profound effect on your style?

David Mamet, for the economy of words he uses, and the rhythm he achieves through words. Also Wendy Wasserstein, for the humanity she infuses in her characters. She's not afraid to show their flaws, which helps the audience see themselves.

What do you hope to achieve with this work?
I hope young people will realize competing with their friends is fine as long as they don't go overboard. When you're young and have the same interests, or play in the same sports, or perform in the arts, it's important to enjoy those activities together and share in each other's accomplishments. This is how we learn to respect each other's differences as well as our strengths and weaknesses.

What were the biggest challenges involved in the writing of this play?
I worked very hard at not making one of the girls appear as too critical or mean. I wanted to show how one girl's obsession with Adele, and her dream of singing like Adele, is hurting her friendship with another girl. I also wanted to show how each girl is vulnerable in different ways.

What are the most common mistakes that occur in productions of your work?
I'm very specific in my plays about the props I use. I make sure the props can be easily found or obtained. However, sometimes the props that are used in productions of my work are not what I had in mind. The props are important because they often motivate actions. I'm specific about props because they help actors make certain choices. Maybe I'm being overly sensitive because I'm the playwright. However, the props aren't "throwaways" that can be replaced with objects that are different than what I wrote in the plays.

What inspired you to become a playwright?
Ever since I was a kid I've always loved the sound of words. I also was introduced to Shakespeare when I was young. My parents took me and my siblings to a "Shakespeare in the Park" festival that was held each summer in the town where I grew up. I loved watching all these bigger than life characters in an outdoor setting. I loved the spectacle. At some point, I decided I wanted to write plays like that.

How did you research the subject?
I attended an actual middle school talent show in which my niece and several of her friends performed. After my niece told me about the "backstage drama" that had taken place, I started thinking about friendships and competition, and how overly competitive friends can get.

Shakespeare gave advice to the players in *Hamlet*; if you could give advice to your cast what would it be?
Have fun! It's a play—so play! Even with a serious play, you can enjoy the experience. I know I expect a lot of younger actors in my plays. I want you to bring your experiences, feelings, and points of views to the characters you play. I want you to find your own truths in the roles you take on. I want you to be authentic, and show vulnerability. I want you to be honest. The audience will respond positively to you when you're honest. Keep it real—even when you're acting.

About the Author

Kenyon Brown is an award-winning playwright whose productions include *Pillow Fight, Notification, All A-Twitter, In View of, Goodbye, Room, The Roof Needs Replacing*. He has been produced in SF, NYC, and LA as well as internationally. Several of his plays for young actors and audiences are available from YouthPLAYS: *All-A-Twitter, Goodbye, Room, Hi, We Thought You Were Dead, My Big Adele Moment* and *The Zombie Effect*. His monologue for young actors, *Annatude*, is available at AuditionArt: The Internet's Greatest Monologue Database. His professional theatre experience includes working at Circle Repertory Company in NYC. He was awarded the Hopwood Award for Drama from the University of Michigan. He is a member of The Playwrights' Center, The Dramatists Guild of America, TCG, and The Writer's Center of Indiana.

MY LITTLE BROTHER

A short dramedy monologue by
Dan Berkowitz

CAST OF CHARACTERS

TEEN-AGED KID, male or female, any age between 13 and
18.

(A TEEN-AGED KID, male or female, any age between 13 and 18, walks onstage and addresses the audience.)

TEEN-AGED KID: My little brother is the ugliest kid in the whole entire world. I mean it. Go to Wikipedia, enter the word "ugly," and there's a picture of my brother. He's, like, a foot shorter than me, but he weighs about a thousand pounds more. He wears big dorky glasses. His hair...looks like a dog was digging for a bone in it. He has lips that look like big globs of meat. A friend of mine once said they looked like liver lips. I started to call him "Liverlips" but my mom told me to cut it out. He just smiled. He always smiles. Always. No matter what happens. I mean, how not-cool is that? And he drools. Makes me want to throw up.

He got this sweatshirt for Christmas two years ago? He took a marker and printed "King of the Dorks" on the front of it in big block letters. Seriously. See, when he first heard the word Dorks, he thought they were, like, some alien life form out of *Star Trek* and that they were, like, really smart? And he wouldn't change his mind, no matter how many times I tried to tell him that was lame. So then he decided he wanted to be King of the Dorks. I mean, how dorky is that? It's, like, dork squared. Cubed. No, it's dorkdom to the tenth power. Whatever that means. Of course, he misspelled "King" so the sweatshirt actually says "Kink of the Dorks," which is even more ridiculous. And he wears it everywhere, and it's falling apart, but he won't throw it away, and he's convinced that when people stare at him they're thinking he's the coolest kid around. I mean, really...?

He calls me "Turtle" because I like to wear a hoodie and he says it makes me look like a turtle. How dumb is that? And I can't call him "Liverlips" but Mom never says anything about him calling me "Turtle." You cannot believe how embarrassing it is when I'm, like, standing on the sidewalk with a group of my friends at school or stuff, waiting for my mom to pick me up, and she drives up and my brother yells out the window of the car, "Hey, Turtle!" and then gives that moron laugh of his. I just want to die. Or kill him. Or both.

He always comes with Mom when she picks me up, or drives me anywhere. I've asked her a million zillion times not to bring him—especially when we're giving a ride to some of my friends—but she always says she has to bring him because she can't leave him alone and I should just deal with it.

But I've <u>been</u> dealing with it all my life. Well, since I was five, which is when he was born. It seems that no matter what I do, or how much I accomplish, <u>he</u> always has to come first, and the spotlight always has to be put on <u>him</u>.

For example: last spring, I got the second lead in the school play? Which was, like, a really big deal. I mean, <u>every</u>one wanted to be in that play so it was really competitive, more people auditioned for it than ever before in the whole entire history of the school. And I got the part. The second lead! But, of course, when I come home all excited and everything, and call the whole family into the living room to announce that I'm going to be a star, what happens? My little brother looks at me through those big dorky glasses and goes, "<u>Second</u> lead? Why aren't you the <u>first</u> lead?" And then he gives that moron laugh. And Mom and Dad smile and laugh and turn to him with this adoring look as if he's just been sooooo clever. And suddenly <u>my</u> news—my <u>big</u> news, a real accomplishment—is, like, nothing. Sometimes it's like I'm not even there!

I mean, why don't I ever get any credit for what I do? I've been in lots of plays and stuff at school, and I've been pretty good, if I say so myself. And it's not easy. I mean, do you know how hard it is to learn lines? How hard it is to learn a <u>monologue</u>? And to walk out in front of a bunch of strangers—or even worse, a bunch of your friends—and, like, pretend you're someone else who's totally different from you while you're trying to remember all the stuff you memorized and where you're supposed to stand and what you're supposed to do with your hands? It's really hard, but it's something I love, and I spend a lot of time practicing, and my friends and my teachers and the drama coach all think I'm good at it, but my mom and dad hardly ever say a word. But whenever my little brother does anything—<u>anything!</u>—they're all over him with "Oh, wasn't that terrific!" "Oh, isn't he wonderful!" "Oh, isn't that great?" And it's gotten worse. Last month, he was picked to lead the Pledge of Allegiance at a parent-teacher meeting— the Pledge of Allegiance, for heaven's sake! —and the way my parents were gushing over him, and congratulating him on remembering all the words, and telling him how well he'd done it and how proud they were of him, you'd think he...he'd just played Hamlet...for the President...and won an Oscar for it!

It's not fair! But it's always been like that, ever since he was born. I had to go stay with Aunt Maddie and Uncle Walt for a whole month when he was born. They're cool, but I missed being home—I was only five. And I missed seeing Mom and Dad for so long. Later on, they said they were sorry, but that it was for the best, cause there was so much going on with my brother right after he was born, y'know, at the hospital and doctors and stuff.

They've always paid a lot more attention to him than they did to me. Most of the time I didn't really mind, I guess. I mean, he <u>needed</u> a lot of attention, cause he couldn't do a lot of stuff. And he got sick a lot, and had to keep going back to the hospital. I used to think it was kind of cool to go to the hospital, cause they had these beds that could go up and down, and you could watch TV all the time, and you could even sit up in bed just by pushing a button. But I guess if you <u>have</u> to do it all the time, it's probably not a lot of fun.

Anyway, I don't know what's wrong this time, but I can tell Mom's been crying a lot. Of course, she says she hasn't. She says she's got allergies and they make her eyes water, but I know that's a crock. A couple of days ago, I overheard one of the doctors say it's a miracle he lived this long, and they should be grateful for the time they had with him, and they should "prepare themselves" — whatever that means. He's been really sick a couple of times before, but this seems, I don't know...different.

And there's a part of me that's thinking that if, this time, he doesn't make it, maybe we can just be a regular family, and maybe Mom and Dad won't always be so stressed out, and maybe we can do normal stuff like my friends' families do. And there's a part of me that's kind of...almost...a little bit...hoping for that. Y'know? But then I feel really bad, because while my brother is really a pain, he's, well, my brother. Y'know?

Sometimes life really sucks.

The Author Speaks

What inspired you to write this play?
A very old Frenchman who directed me in a Molière play many years ago opened his autobiography with the line, "My mother was the ugliest woman I ever saw." He's been dead some years now, and it's been even longer since I read the book, but the line suddenly occurred to me one day, and I thought "Hmmmm, I wonder what it would be like to open a play with something like that." I didn't want to use the exact line, so I substituted "little brother" for "mother"—and then I was off to the races!

Was the structure of the play influenced by any other work?
I wanted to write a monologue that engaged the audience directly, by having the character talk right to them. In that sense, it's not unlike the monologues in plays such as Kurt Vonnegut's *Happy Birthday, Wanda June* and my own *Bodysurfing in the Sea of Contagion*. It's not a "To be or not to be" soliloquy where the character is musing aloud—it's an in-your-face diatribe to whomever the actor decides the audience will represent.

Have you dealt with the same theme in other works that you have written?
Love, and the difficulty communicating it, is always part of the subtext of my plays. My other works which YouthPLAYS publishes—*Pretty* and *Silver Linings*—have the same sort of theme going on.

What writers have had the most profound effect on your style?
Every writer I've ever read has had some impact—even when I hate the work and determine <u>never</u> to write like that person! I admire Truman Capote for the elegance and simplicity of his prose; Tennessee Williams for the passion and poetry. Most of

all, I admire writers who can combine the funny with the wrenching, who can make you laugh right before they tear your heart out — then make you laugh again.

What do you hope to achieve with this work?

Do what the writers I admire most do: entertain an audience by making them laugh, while at the same time moving them by showing them another side to the characters.

What are the most common mistakes that occur in productions of your work?

I sound like a broken record when I say this, but I don't care: please don't "do" anything unless you absolutely have to. Just say the words — and mean them — and make sure the audience understands what you're saying.

So many times, actors don't feel they're acting enough, and directors don't feel they're directing enough, unless there's lots of "stuff" going on: moving around the set, smoking a cigarette, playing with a deck of cards. Sometimes a physical activity is necessary to the play, but if so it would be indicated in the script. Sometimes a physical activity can be useful in illustrating a character's traits — if it doesn't distract from the words. But when stuff is put in simply for the sake of doing something — and doesn't relate directly to what's going on in the play — it's a distraction and can ruin the whole play.

There was a very funny episode of *Glee*, in which a "famous Hollywood actor" who'd been a student at the school came back and conducted a "Master Class" in acting. Of course, the only reason he was famous was that he was a spokesman for some truly awful website, and had appeared in about a million bad commercials for it. As the kids hung on his every word, he pompously proclaimed that the key to great acting — great acting — was never paying attention to what the other actors in the play were doing, because that might distract you from doing what you'd decided to do ahead of time, which in his case was almost always eating a roast beef sandwich.

It's that kind of eager but clueless "Hey, wouldn't it be great if I did [fill in the blank] while I say my line?" that drives me crazy.

And, oh yeah, please don't add things like "Uh" or "Well" or "Y'know" or any similar words, grunts, or other sounds to the lines. Believe me, I know how to write "Uh" and "Well" and "Y'know" and if I wanted a character to say one of them, I would have written it. Sometimes an actor will say, "But I'm not comfortable saying that line. Can't I change it?" To which I quote the great acting teacher Stella Adler, who used to say "Your job as an actor is not to be 'comfortable'—it's to be right." Figure out why your character says what he or she says—not what you think the character ought to say—and that will give you your biggest clue as to how to play the play.

What inspired you to become a playwright?
I wanted to be rich and famous. The preceding sentence is an example of "irony." Seriously, as with most of life, I fell into it by accident. When I was in my 20s, I was the producer/director/emcee of a weekly musical and comedy cabaret revue. We did a new show each week, with rotating casts (the musical director, choreographer, and I were the only constants), and by mid-week, I'd know that we needed, say, a minute-long "thing" to cover a costume change here, or a three-minute comedy sketch to liven up the show there—and I'd write it. Flash forward to some years later, after the musical director, who'd appeared in the wildly successful revue *A...My Name Is Alice*, agreed to be in the sequel, to be called *A...My Name Is Still Alice*. The creators were looking for sketch material, she gave them my name, and they wound up using more sketches by me than by any other writer. The show

started at the Old Globe Theatre in San Diego before transferring to New York, and I got glowing reviews from the California papers for my stuff. Suddenly I was a writer in demand: I was asked to write some things for television, to doctor an off-Broadway musical, eventually to be the LA Regional Rep for The Dramatists Guild. All from writing short sketches for a weekly revue. You see what I mean when I say "by accident"?

Shakespeare gave advice to the players in *Hamlet*; if you could give advice to your cast what would it be?
It was so long ago I don't remember who it was, but someone once said "The more the actor cries, the less the audience will." It stunned me at the time, because I was very young, and was a performer, and prided myself on being able to bring forth tears at will — that was <u>acting</u>!

But as I watched more and more plays, I found that when actors succumbed to the emotion of the moment, and let their characters fall to pieces and blubber and weep, it didn't affect me nearly as much as when they played the character trying to <u>hold off</u> falling to pieces, trying to keep the emotions in check, trying to "rise above" the pathos. When you let yourself surrender to emotion, it's a form of self-pity, which I personally find very unattractive.

My Little Brother can be played as one long, tearful, self-pitying whine, or it can come from another place: a place of anger, perhaps, of frustration combined with love and determination, a place where the character recognizes the unfairness of the situation and isn't happy with it — but at the same time realizes it's no one's "fault" and you just have to make the best of it.

Personally, I find that approach infinitely more interesting, both to watch — and to play.

How was the first production different from the vision that you created in your mind?

Once, when I was directing a play and wanted the actor to strive to overcome the character's challenges (rather than yielding to them), I came up with the phrase "If you try to succeed, you may fail; but if you try to fail, you will always succeed." By that I meant that if you stay upbeat and positive, and strive to push forward no matter how hard it may be, hopefully you'll succeed—but you still may fail. If, on the other hand, you give in to the obstacles, and allow yourself to surrender to hopelessness and despair, you will definitely succeed in failing. To me, it's much more interesting when someone fights, even if he or she eventually fails.

When I wrote *My Little Brother*, I envisioned the character as someone who fought to be as clear-eyed and unemotional as possible, and who only at the very end, just barely, lets us see how much he or she loves the little brother of the title, and how devastating it will be to lose him. In the initial production, the actress and director chose to take a more emotional route, which can certainly be justified, but wasn't what I had in mind when I wrote it.

About the Author

Dan Berkowitz is Co-Chair of The Alliance of Los Angeles Playwrights, and is the former Los Angeles Regional Rep of The Dramatists Guild of America, the professional association of playwrights, composers, and lyricists. His writing for the stage has been produced off-Broadway, in major regional theatres, in college and amateur theatres throughout the United States, and in Canada. He is the author of several optioned screenplays, and was principal scriptwriter for The Movie Channel's hosted format with Robert Osborne. A former Senior Story Analyst for RHI Entertainment, a division of Hallmark, Dan is a consultant for stage, film, and television scripts. In addition to writing, Dan has produced and/or directed scores of plays, musicals, and cabaret revues, as well as several seasons of syndicated television programming, and a raft of commercials and industrial and educational videos. His website is http://danberkowitz.com.

THREE FIRST KISSES

A short dramedy by
Tim Bohn

CAST OF CHARACTERS

KATIE, an eighth grade girl.

JEN, an eighth grade girl.

SHELLY, an eighth grade girl.

SETTING

Katie's bedroom, right after school. There is a bed, a desk with make-up, nail polish, hairspray and books scattered on top of it, and a chair for the desk.

(KATIE, JEN, and SHELLY enter Katie's room, laughing and talking about their day at school. There is a bed, a desk, and various stuffed animals, etc.)

KATIE: No way!

SHELLY: Way.

KATIE: Libby and Tyler?

JEN: Hotness!

KATIE: Sucking face?

JEN: I would totally make out with Tyler Phillips.

SHELLY: No, it was Tyler Larson.

KATIE: Eew!

JEN: Nasty.

(Jen and Katie drop their backpacks and sit on the bed. Shelly puts her things on the desk and sits at the chair.)

SHELLY: No, it's sweet!

JEN: Katie?

KATIE: Tyler is just gross, Shelly.

SHELLY: Katie, I can't believe you! You and Jen are just...

KATIE: What?

JEN: Yeah, what are we?

SHELLY: Jealous.

JEN: Of Tyler? Nooooo!

KATIE: Seriously, Shell, I'd never kiss Tyler.

SHELLY: Maybe not, but you would kiss somebody.

JEN: Ooooh, this is getting juicy! Who is it?

KATIE: Just forget about it, okay? You guys want something to eat? I'm starving.

JEN: Go ahead, run down to your mommy and get some

cookies. We'll stay up here and talk about you.

KATIE: Hey!

(She hits Jen with a pillow.)

Fine, I'll just stay right here. You two have to go home sometime!

JEN: Right, good point. Shelly can tell me about this mystery man on the way home.

KATIE: Shelly, why did you —

SHELLY: I didn't say anything!

KATIE: You promised!

SHELLY: I didn't say anything. Jen, I didn't say anything to you, did I?

JEN: No. Nobody told me anything! I'm waiting. Who is it? Come on, Shelly, spill the beans!

SHELLY: Don't look at me!

JEN: Come on. Katie won't tell me anything —

KATIE: It's nobody, okay?!

JEN: Just tell me — you know you will sooner or later.

KATIE: It's nobody, I told you.

SHELLY: Jen, leave her alone.

JEN: I just want a name. Then I'll shut up, promise!

SHELLY: Drop it, okay? I'm sorry I never should've —

KATIE: It's nobody! Nobody, ever. Nobody wants to date me or kiss me or talk to me. Okay? I've never been kissed by anybody. I'm the only girl in the 8th grade that can say that, right? Happy? Is that what you wanted to hear?

JEN: I'm sorry —

KATIE: So maybe Shelly is right. Maybe I am jealous of Libby. At least Tyler likes her.

SHELLY: Come on, that's not what—

KATIE: How embarrassing! I can't believe this.

SHELLY: It's no big deal.

JEN: Yeah, jeez, lots of people haven't—

KATIE: I'm gonna get some chips or something. You want anything? No? Fine.

> *(Katie quickly exits before she starts crying. Jen and Shelly sit quietly for a moment.)*

JEN: Wow. That sucked.

SHELLY: Why do you have to be so mean?

JEN: What? What did I do?

SHELLY: You just kept pushing her. She obviously didn't—

JEN: Don't start in on me. You two are keeping secrets!

SHELLY: Not secrets—

JEN: Secrets! You two are talking about boys and kissing and not kissing and not telling me about it. Secrets.

SHELLY: It just came up today, that's all. I'm sure she would have told you.

JEN: Told me what?

SHELLY: You know.

JEN: Not really. She's never been kissed?

SHELLY: Nope.

JEN: Never?

SHELLY: No, never had a boyfriend, nothing.

JEN: So she's embarrassed.

SHELLY: Well, yeah.

JEN: It's no big deal, really. Is it?

SHELLY: Well, she thinks so.

JEN: But do you?

SHELLY: Well, kinda.

JEN: What do you mean, "Kinda"?

SHELLY: It's kind of a big deal. I mean if you've never been kissed and all your friends are talking about it and even Libby and Tyler...

JEN: Yeah, I guess so.

SHELLY: It's hard. You feel like there's something wrong, you know?

JEN: She does? That's not right, she —

SHELLY: I do, too.

JEN: You?

SHELLY: Yeah. It's hard being around everybody. Like there's this secret club that everybody is in but me and —

JEN: You?! You and Kevin went out for like 3 months.

SHELLY: Well, kinda. We held hands.

JEN: He never kissed you?

SHELLY: Nope.

JEN: Why not?

SHELLY: I dunno.

JEN: But —

SHELLY: A couple times I thought he was going to. But he got really pale and sweaty and left both times. I think he was scared.

JEN: Really? That's hilarious!

SHELLY: See? There you go again! You're so mean.

JEN: Come on — it's funny! You wanted to kiss him and he was too scared?

SHELLY: It's scary! I was scared too. I could've kissed him and I didn't. It's terrifying!

JEN: You're terrified of Kevin?

SHELLY: No, not him. Haven't you ever worried that a boy wouldn't kiss you back? Or that he'd tell his friends about it? Or that he wouldn't like it? Or that you wouldn't like it? It's like the whole world is watching and if you do anything stupid or wrong or silly your whole life is ruined.

JEN: That's a little extreme.

SHELLY: Well, maybe. But that's how I felt. So, Katie isn't alone. I've never had my first kiss either.

JEN: It's no big deal.

SHELLY: What was yours like?

JEN: Don't—

SHELLY: Come on. I told you my terrible secret. Who was it? Caleb? Or was it Dan?

JEN: I don't want to talk about it.

SHELLY: Why not? Chicken?

JEN: Let's go see what Katie is up to, I'm worried about her.

(Jen makes a move for the door, but Shelly cuts her off.)

SHELLY: Oh no you don't! You were the one complaining about us having secrets. Now you have to spill.

JEN: Fine. Neither.

SHELLY: Who then?

(Jen shrugs.)

Nobody? You haven't kissed anybody?

JEN: Guess not.

SHELLY: Holy crap.

JEN: Hey!

SHELLY: No, this is huge!

JEN: What? You gonna tell everybody?

SHELLY: Not everybody. Just Katie. Katie! KATIE!

JEN: SHHHHH!

SHELLY: You gotta tell her! You saw how freaked out she was.

KATIE: *(Off.)* I'm coming!

JEN: Not cool.

SHELLY: Here she comes. Shh!

(Katie enters carrying a bag of chips. Jen sits with her head down on the bed while Shelly bounces with excitement at the desk. Katie stares at them for a moment.)

KATIE: What?

JEN: Nothing.

SHELLY: Jen has a secret!

JEN: No, I don't.

KATIE: Guys, I don't feel like talking about it so…maybe you should —

SHELLY: Jen never kissed anybody!

JEN: Shut up!

KATIE: What?!

SHELLY: Never! Not once.

JEN: Neither has Shelly!

SHELLY: That's true! Me neither!

KATIE: What about Kevin?

SHELLY: He panicked. Every time. No kisses!

KATIE: Caleb? Dan?

JEN: Nope.

SHELLY: Neither one!

KATIE: What? Why not?

JEN: They both tried. But...

KATIE: Shelly? What happened?

SHELLY: I dunno—she never told me this part. What happened?

JEN: It, well, they tried to kiss me but I kinda...hit them.

SHELLY: Cool!

KATIE: Hit them?

JEN: Caleb got real pushy so I smacked him. Dan wasn't so bad, so I just sorta pushed his face like, you know, into the ground.

SHELLY: That is awesome.

JEN: No, it isn't awesome. Who is ever gonna want to date the girl that beats up everyone that tries to kiss her?

KATIE: And you?

SHELLY: Me?

KATIE: Yeah, you never kissed anybody?

SHELLY: Oh, no.

KATIE: We're pathetic.

SHELLY: No! Don't you see?

JEN: See what?

SHELLY: This is all perfectly normal.

KATIE: NOT kissing is normal? Everybody but us is probably making out right now.

SHELLY: No way. For all we know, Libby and Tyler are the ONLY people in the 8th grade that have ever kissed anybody!

JEN: She's got a point.

SHELLY: I know, right?

KATIE: Wow. This is a lot to take in.

(Katie sits on the bed and begins to eat chips as she contemplates what she has just learned.)

JEN: It feels good to talk about it, right?

(Jen takes a chip and munches on it while she thinks.)

SHELLY: It's nice to be, you know, not alone.

(Shelly takes a handful of chips and eats them while staring off into space. After a few moments, the chips are gone.)

KATIE: No more chips.

JEN: I'm gonna go. I'm gonna go to Dan's house and kiss him.

SHELLY: Why?

JEN: Just to get it over with.

KATIE: I'll call Kevin.

SHELLY: No!

KATIE: What? Why not?

SHELLY: No, no, no, no! It's wrong!

JEN: It's not wrong, we're just scared. Once we kiss one boy the rest will be easy.

KATIE: Right. I'm tired of worrying about it!

JEN: Text me later, let me know how it goes.

(Katie gets out her phone and starts dialing. Jen grabs her backpack and heads for the door. Shelly grabs hair spray off the desk and blocks Jen from leaving, threatening her with the hairspray.)

SHELLY: No! I mean it. Sit down or Jen gets it.

JEN: Are you nuts?

SHELLY: SIT! Katie, hang up the phone.

JEN: She's psycho.

SHELLY: Hang. Up. The. Phone.

  (Katie hangs up.)

You, sit.

  (Jen sits.)

KATIE: Okay, crazy, what's up?

SHELLY: Stop and think. Don't go rushing off to kiss some boy to make it EASY. It's not supposed to be EASY!

JEN: What do you know? You've never—

SHELLY: Neither have you! Or you! Why not?

JEN: We went over this—

SHELLY: No, we didn't. We talked about being scared, but WHY?

KATIE: Shelly, it's just dumb. There's nothing to be scared of.

SHELLY: There is! Kissing someone is a big deal. Who have you kissed?

KATIE: Nobody.

SHELLY: Your mom? Your dad?

JEN: That's not the same.

SHELLY: No, but it means something. It has to mean something. That's the point. That's why we never kissed any of those boys.

JEN: It's not the same as kissing your family.

SHELLY: Why not?

JEN: They're your family.

SHELLY: You love them.

JEN: Eew.

SHELLY: You love them — you don't want to date them. Gross.

KATIE: Yeah, that's nasty.

SHELLY: That's not what I'm saying. I'm saying it means SOMETHING.

KATIE: Well, yeah, goodnight or goodbye or whatever.

SHELLY: No, it means you love them and trust them.

JEN: So I shouldn't kiss somebody until I'm married? No way.

KATIE: I'm not going wait for marriage. That's nuts.

SHELLY: Fine, go kiss everybody in school. See if I care.

KATIE: I'm not gonna kiss everybody.

SHELLY: Go ahead. Ruin it!

JEN: Ruin what?

SHELLY: Your first kiss!

JEN: I just want to get it over with!

KATIE: For real.

JEN: I just don't want it to be, I dunno...

KATIE: Such a big deal.

JEN: Right.

> *(Shelly slumps into the chair. Katie grabs her phone again and Jen grabs her bag.)*

SHELLY: Well, I'm gonna wait.

JEN: Until you're married? Have fun.

SHELLY: No.

KATIE: Wait for what?

SHELLY: I'm going to wait until it IS a big deal. I'm going to wait until whoever it is doesn't make me uncomfortable and look like they're gonna faint, or make me want to hit them, or whatever. I'm going to wait until it means something. I'm gonna have an amazing first kiss.

(Katie sits on the bed.)

KATIE: Do you ever fantasize about like, what it will be like?

SHELLY: Only all the time.

KATIE: I want it to be snowing. Under a street light at night, our breath steaming around us, the world just disappearing around us as we kiss. Cold noses, warm lips...

SHELLY: I always wanted it to be in a coffee shop.

JEN: You don't drink coffee.

SHELLY: No, but he will. And I'll have tea. We'll be holding hands and talking. We keep leaning closer over the table, totally into our conversation about a book or something, and then we're almost touching and he leans in, our eyes closed, our lips touch...

(Shelly and Katie sigh with dreamy looks in their eyes. After a moment, Jen plops on the bed.)

JEN: In a photo booth.

SHELLY: What?

JEN: I want it to be in a photo booth. Like at the mall with the strips of four pictures that come out. You know? Anyway, we'll be in there and the first picture will be me on his lap making silly faces, the second picture is me tousling his hair, the third picture is us staring at each other and he has his hand on my cheek like this, then the fourth picture is us kissing. I'll have that picture forever to remind me of my first kiss.

(Katie, Jen, and Shelly stare off into space imagining their perfect first kisses. After a moment they sigh in unison. Blackout. End of play.)

The Author Speaks

What inspired you to write this play?
As a teacher, I deal with students every day. While I teach on the university level, I am often doing outreach work at high schools and middle schools and this serves as a reminder of my time there. When I think back to middle school and high school, everything seemed to revolve around these milestones. The pressure to keep up, to be normal, is enormous. The further removed I got from those times, the more my peers opened up to me about their experiences, and I soon learned that everybody felt the same way! This play is that moment when they learn they are not alone, that they are normal, and that it is going to be okay.

What writers have had the most profound effect on your style?
John Patrick Shanley is my hero. I find him unbearably romantic, but not in a pretty way at all. He shows us how hard it is to love someone, and how impossible it is to be happy the way fairy tales tell us it is supposed to be. He explores friendships, families, romance, marriage, and even professional relationships and shows us the dark side of what we always think of as beautiful; and he does it with poetry, style, and humor. The truth in everything he writes, no matter how fantastic, is something I try to find in my work.

What do you hope to achieve with this work?
It is my hope that *Three First Kisses* will touch actors and audiences alike and help them see that they aren't alone— everyone has the same fears, insecurities, and frustrations that they are feeling. Armed with this, maybe they can take the path that the three girls in the play do and stand strong against peer pressure and wait until they are ready for whatever comes next.

What were the biggest challenges involved in the writing of this play?
Being a middle-aged man, it is sometimes difficult to find the voice of an eighth grade girl.

What are the most common mistakes that occur in productions of your work?
I tend to write as minimally as possible, meaning I write very few stage directions. I try to make the required action of the play as clear as possible through dialogue. Sometimes, this isn't successful. Words are liquid in many ways, and sometimes the action I intended to indicate through the dialogue is misinterpreted (in my mind). While I may consider that a mistake, it's also part of the beauty of live theatre. You will never see a play done the same way twice!

What inspired you to become a playwright?
I've always been an artist. In school I played viola, trombone, tuba, baritone, electric bass, sang in the choir, acted in shows, painted, sculpted, everything I could. Creating art isn't optional for me. I have things I need to say, and writing plays is the way I am best able to communicate my ideas. Of all of the forms of art I practice, I feel that live theatre gives me the best palette to entertain, educate, and hopefully influence people and maybe make this world a better place.

Shakespeare gave advice to the players in *Hamlet*; if you could give advice to your cast what would it be?
Remember these girls are friends, close friends, BFFs. Their insults, teasing, and threats all come from a place of love. Avoid the temptation to make it too serious, especially towards the end.

About the Author

Tim Bohn is an Assistant Professor in the Arkansas State University's Department of Theatre, teaching courses in Directing, Playwriting, Acting, and Script Analysis and whatever else needs doing. He received a Master of Fine Arts degree in Directing from the University of North Carolina at Greensboro and a Bachelor of Arts degree in Theatre from the University of Wisconsin – Parkside. Tim is a proud member of the Dramatists Guild, Southeastern Theatre Conference, and serves as Chair of the Ten-Minute Play Festival for SETC. In addition to writing plays, teaching, and puttering in the garden, Tim is an enormous nerd and really likes to play online games and board games. He lives with his wife (Lisa) and two children (Eli and Wyatt) in Jonesboro, Arkansas.

ERASING THE BRAIN

A short dramedy by
Nina Mansfield

CAST OF CHARACTERS

ELLEN, a thirteen-year-old girl.

MATTIE, Ellen's ten-year-old brother.

VOICE OF MOTHER, an offstage voice.

TIME

The present.

PLACE

A living room or family room. The room has a television console with a video game system, which can be suggested by having Mattie face the audience while playing the video game.

The video game controller can be replaced with a handheld gaming device or remote control device, in which case, the play could be staged on a very, very simple set.

ACKNOWLEDGMENTS

The play premiered in April 2010 as part of Turtle Shell Productions' 8-Minute Madness YouthFest (New York, NY), directed by Joel Haberli.

(Lights up on MATTIE, who is sitting, engrossed in a video game. The SOUNDS of a video game can be heard, and the light from the television flickers on Mattie's face. ELLEN storms into the living room. She is holding her diary, which she slams down on a nearby table.)

ELLEN: Just who do you think you are?

MATTIE: If you hold on two seconds, I will be...master of the universe.

(Ellen grabs the controller away from him; he tries to snatch it back.)

Hey Ellen, give that back.

ELLEN: Why should I?

MATTIE: I was about to reach a new high... *(An electronic rendition of MOZART'S "REQUIEM" signals the end of the game:)* ...score.

ELLEN: Put out your hands.

MATTIE: What? Why?

ELLEN: I want to see your hands, Mattie.

MATTIE: No. You're crazy.

(They struggle. Ellen grabs his hands, and flips them up to look at the palms. He closes his hands into fists.)

ELLEN: Open them.

MATTIE: You can't make me.

ELLEN: I said, open them.

(She begins to squeeze his wrists tighter, until he is forced to open his hands up.)

MATTIE: OK, OK. Just stop. That hurts.

(Ellen examines his palms for a moment, and then throws down his hands.)

ELLEN: I knew it. I knew it. I'm telling. Mom!

MATTIE: She's not home yet.

ELLEN: She should be home—

MATTIE: She's on a date.

ELLEN: Oh.

MATTIE: With...what's his name...Hank.

ELLEN: Oh.

MATTIE: Again.

(The two are silent for a moment.)

I don't think Hank really exists, do you? I hope he doesn't. I hope he's just...I hope he's just like her...imaginary friend or something. Like I used to have.

ELLEN: Whatever. I'm still telling.

MATTIE: Telling what? What did I do?

ELLEN: You know perfectly well what you did.

MATTIE: What? I didn't do anything.

ELLEN: Then what's that white stuff on your hands?

MATTIE: *(Looking at his hands:)* What stuff?

ELLEN: That fine dusting of white powder.

MATTIE: I dunno.

ELLEN: I do. You see, I was on to you. I could sniff you out a mile away. You thought you could be sneaky. You thought you could cover your tracks. Putting my diary back under my pillow. Placing the key back into my desk. So first I hid the key. That probably screwed up your little plan, didn't it? But then, I knew something was wrong. The way it was laying there, upside down, under my pillow. I would've never left it that way. What did you use...a bobby pin or something? Some tool from your Swiss Army knife? Whatever it was, it scratched up the lock. You probably didn't notice that, did you? So I decided to catch you in the act. Baby power. A light dusting inside the pages. Now, it's on your hands. There's my proof.

(Ellen pulls the controlling device out of the video game machine, dangles it in front of Mattie for a second, and then begins to walk away.)

MATTIE: He doesn't like you.

ELLEN: *(She stops in her tracks:)* What?

MATTIE: Evan Marshall. The man of your dreams. The only boy you'll ever love. He doesn't like you.

ELLEN: Why you little...

(Ellen lunges at him; Mattie jumps out of her way.)

MATTIE: Don't hit, please don't hit me. I heard them talking, that's all.

ELLEN: What? When? Who?

MATTIE: Sheila Cassidy and her group. The ones that sit at the back of the bus. The ones that wear all that makeup.

ELLEN: When was this? What did they say? When were you ever sitting at the back of the bus?

MATTIE: Last week. You were staying late for band practice. Robbie dared me. But they kicked me out, so I just sat a few rows up, and heard their whole conversation. Sheila said that Evan likes Amy Steinem. That she saw them kissing on the playground last week. And I wouldn't have paid any attention at all except, well...

(He holds up his hands sheepishly.)

ELLEN: You're just making this up to hurt me.

MATTIE: Do you think it's true?

ELLEN: What?

MATTIE: That there's only one guy for you? That Evan Marshall will be the only boy you ever love?

ELLEN: You are the worst little brother that anyone could ever have.

(She leaves, taking the controller and her diary with her.)

MATTIE: *(Calling after her:)* Oh, come on. Give it back.

ELLEN: *(Off:)* Not on your life.

MATTIE: Please!

ELLEN: *(Off:)* No!

MATTIE: It's not like I read the whole thing. Just a few of the entries from last week. You can't really blame me. It's what little brothers are supposed to do. We're supposed to read our big sisters' diaries. It's like a rule.

ELLEN: *(Off:)* I'm not listening to you.

MATTIE: If you give it back, I promise never to read it again. Cross my heart and hope to die. Never, ever, ever.

ELLEN: *(Re-entering:)* It's a little too late for that.

MATTIE: I'll go to confession and say a dozen Hail Marys.

ELLEN: We're not Catholic.

MATTIE: I can still confess. I don't think you have to be Catholic to get your soul wiped clean. And when my soul's wiped clean, you have to forgive me. Because God has.

ELLEN: Nice try. You're not getting it back.

(She starts to leave.)

MATTIE: *(Desperate:)* So...so, I'll erase my brain. Forget what I read.

ELLEN: You can't erase your brain.

MATTIE: Sure you can.

ELLEN: You can't force yourself to forget.

MATTIE: I forget stuff all the time.

ELLEN: It's not the same thing.

MATTIE: Last week, I forgot all about the Battle of Bunker Hill during my history test.

ELLEN: That just makes you stupid.

MATTIE: And I always forget my lunch money at home.

ELLEN: What's your point?

MATTIE: If you don't think about something — like ever — it just vanishes from your brain. Poof. Like it was never there. I bet if you wanted to, you could forget all about Evan Marshall.

ELLEN: *(Starting to walk away again:)* You just don't understand anything.

MATTIE: Like Mom. Forgetting Dad.

ELLEN: *(She stops in her tracks, and turns to Mattie:)* Mom hasn't forgotten Dad. Why would you say something like that?

MATTIE: Hank.

(Ellen starts being the big sister. She goes to comfort Mattie.)

ELLEN: Just because she's — she hasn't forgotten Dad, OK.

MATTIE: I'm starting to. I mean, not forget-forget. Just little things. Like that song he used to sing to us. I can't remember the words any more. And how he liked his coffee.

ELLEN: Light and sweet.

MATTIE: Huh?

ELLEN: His coffee.

MATTIE: Do you think she wants to forget?

ELLEN: Maybe just a little. I don't know. I think remembering too much is sometimes just as bad as forgetting. Besides. You might be right. Hank's probably just imaginary. I mean, we've never met him or anything. So it's kind of like he doesn't exist.

(A quiet moment.)

MATTIE: Wait a second...hold on...I think...I can't. Nope. It's gone. I can't remember his name.

ELLEN: Dad's?

MATTIE: No stupid. That boy you were writing about. See, I told you I could forget. Gimme a few days, and I bet I can forget he ever existed.

ELLEN: You are such an idiot.

MATTIE: Can I get it back now? Can I? Can I?

ELLEN: Fine. Just stop bugging me. And if I ever catch you again—

MATTIE: Don't worry. You won't... *(Under breath:)* ...catch me.

ELLEN: What was that?

MATTIE: I promise. I swear, OK.

ELLEN: OK, OK. *(She begins to walk away:)* Except...

MATTIE: What? Except what?

ELLEN: There's one little problem.

MATTIE: Problem?

ELLEN: You see, I hid it somewhere and...

MATTIE: So...

ELLEN: I just can't remember where I hid it.

MATTIE: What do you mean?

ELLEN: I guess I managed to erase my brain.

(Mattie stares at her. Ellen is smiling.)

VOICE OF MOTHER: Kids, I'm home. There's someone here I want you both to meet.

(Ellen's smile fades. Mattie looks worried. Lights fade. End of play.)

The Author Speaks

What inspired you to write this play?

Most of the plays I have written have been for adults; but in addition to writing plays, I also write young adult fiction, and I wanted to write a play for young people. I am never entirely sure what is going to come out when I sit down to write at my computer. I'm also never entirely sure where my inspiration comes from. However, I will say that from age eleven to age seventeen I used to write in my diary practically every day. I would have been absolutely mortified if anyone found it and read it. I also have a brother (older, not younger,) and while he never did steal my diary, I began to imagine what might have happened if he had. So while I didn't recognize it while I was writing the play, looking back I realize that my childhood diary and my brother served as my inspiration.

Have you dealt with the same theme in other works that you have written?

I have not dealt with this theme in any of my other works. In fact, this is currently my only play for young people. It is also one of my more serious plays, as the short plays I write tend to be much more comedic in nature. And while *Erasing the Brain* has many comic moments, I believe the underlying theme — children dealing with the loss of a parent — is certainly very serious. That said, most of my plays deal with characters who are struggling for something and someone or something is standing in their way.

What writers have had the most profound effect on your style?

The list of writers that have had an effect on my style is pretty long. Some of my favorite playwrights are Chekhov, Ibsen and Shakespeare. I consider Chekhov to be the Seinfeld of his age. He found the humor in common, everyday situations. Characters seemed to be doing nothing, and yet, so much is going on in their internal lives. Their lives fall apart as they sit and sip tea. Currently, I teach high school English, and I have had the opportunity to teach plays like **Romeo and Juliet, Hamlet, Othello, Medea, Oedipus** and **Antigone**. It is difficult not to be inspired by these great works while teaching them. The characters in Ancient Greek tragedies have such awe inspiring emotions. They are driven to extremes—murder, revenge, suicide! The same is true of Shakespeare's characters. And while I certainly don't advise any of these behaviors in real life, they are fascinating to watch on stage. As a playwright, I often ask myself, what makes a character go to such extremes? What, for example, might drive a person insane? Or drive a person to murder? My characters don't necessarily go there—my plays generally take a more comic route—but these questions often inspire my work.

What do you hope to achieve with this work?
I wanted to explore the relationship between a brother and sister going through a particularly challenging period in their lives. What starts off as just an argument between siblings, sparked by Mattie's theft of Ellen's diary, turns out to be something else entirely. As someone who works with teenagers, I know that it is often difficult to know what is truly going on with someone. Unless we make an effort to probe deeper, to ask the right questions, we tend to judge people based solely on their behavior. Mattie and Ellen are two kids who clearly have a lot going on, beyond just regular "kid stuff." Oh sure, that is impacting their lives as well. But they've also lost their father, and they are now dealing with the idea of their mother dating. They aren't ready to forget their father, and yet they feel that maybe their mother has moved on too soon. So, while they start off as rivals, battling each other in a way that many siblings do, they discover that they actually need each other to get through this difficult time in their lives.

What are the most common mistakes that occur in productions of your work?

While I have been very pleased with most productions of my work, I think one of the biggest mistakes I've seen occur is when directors ignore or flat out change stage directions. When I write a play, I rarely write in stage directions that aren't essential. I understand that the director is an important part of the theatre process. That said, I have found that some directors are taught to ignore stage directions, and even feel that it is all right to change dialogue or the gender of a character without asking the playwright permission. This is not okay!

What inspired you to become a playwright?

Before I was a playwright, I was an actor. I've spent a great deal of time being in and around theatre productions, so when I started writing, it just felt right to write in dialogue. When I was in college, I spent a summer interning at a wonderful organization in New York City called New Dramatists. While I was there, I got to read stage directions for a number of play readings (both rehearsed and unrehearsed) for works-in-progress. One of my fondest memories from that summer was having the opportunity to read stage directions for a reading of a new play by Robert Anderson, who wrote *Tea and Sympathy*. I was so inspired after the reading, that when I got on the train to go home that evening, I took a crumpled envelope out of my purse and began writing what would eventually become my first produced and published play, *No Epilogue*.

Shakespeare gave advice to the players in *Hamlet*; if you could give advice to your cast what would it be?

Believe in your characters. Make it true. Raise the stakes. Never play things for laughs. The comedy will come from the honesty of the situation. Make things really, really important for your characters. This might not seem like a life or death situation, but for these characters, it is! If it isn't important for your character, then the audience isn't going to care.

How was the first production different from the vision that you created in your mind?

The first production of *Erasing the Brain* was actually very similar to the vision I had in my mind of how it should work. I was lucky in that the play was first produced in New York at a theatre where I have had a number of my short plays performed, and the director was a friend of mine. I attended a number of rehearsals, and the director and I spoke often about his vision and my vision for the play. For me, this was an ideal situation!

About the Author

Nina Mansfield is a playwright and fiction writer whose plays have been produced professionally and by academic and community theatres throughout the United States and in Canada. Her produced plays include: *Au Naturel*; *Bar Car Reverie*; *Bite Me*; *Bona Fide*; *Clean*; *Clown Therapy*; *Crash Bound*; *Erasing the Brain*; *Missed Exit*; *No Epilogue*; *Pedestrian Casualty: Bronx, USA*; *The Ping and the Pong of It*; *Smile*; *Text Misdirected* and *The Tea Exercise*. Nina holds an MA in Educational Theatre with Teaching English 7-12 from New York University and a BA in Theatre and Sociology from Vanderbilt University. She studied acting and directing at the Moscow Art Theatre in Russia and is a member of the Actors' Equity Association and the Screen Actors Guild. She is also a proud member of The Dramatists Guild, the Society of Children's Writers and Illustrators, Mystery Writers of America and Sisters in Crime. Nina currently teaches Drama and English in the state of New York.

LE GOALIE

A short dramedy by
Nelson Yu

CAST OF CHARACTERS

FABRICE, male, 12-year-old hockey goalie.

SHELLY, female, 12-year-old hockey forward.

COACH, pre-recorded man's voice.

JORDAN, pre-recorded teenage hockey player's voice.

ACT I: INTRODUCING FABRICE

SCENE 1: THE GOALIE

(FABRICE, a hyperactive 12-year-old goalie, marches in and squats in front of an imaginary hockey net. He speaks quickly with a Quebecois accent — where "th" is hard to pronounce so "the" becomes "da" and "think" becomes "tink." Also, the grammar is wrong like he still struggles with English sometimes. Hockey players and teams' names can be updated as necessary.)

FABRICE: I can stop anyting! *(Faking a save:)* Sidney Crosby. No problem! *(Faking a save:)* Ilya Kovachuk. See ya! Steven Stamkos!? Hey, how's that Rocket Richard trophy looking? Oh, you need just one more goal. Well too bad, eh! *(Faking a bigger save:)* I'm the best since Patrick Roy. Better than Marc Andre Fleury. Better than that J.S. Giguere guy. And I'm only in peewee. Wait until I get to da pros, huh! I be unstoppable! *(He makes one last big save:)* But I can't stop Shelly Matador. She's too nice. I wish she wasn't cuz I would never let her score on me. They let a girl play hockey because she's that good. She used to be — like my neighbour — until she moved away. Then she played for the other team, the Falcons. But it no matter. She's still my friend. The coach yells at me when Shelly scores on me.

COACH: *(Jokingly:)* HEY, FABRICE. DON'T LET THE GIRL GET TA YA!

FABRICE: But I no care. I know I'm the best. I let one or two in so they think they can beat me. Yeah, let them tink dey can beat Fabrice Allaire! Goalie extraordinaire! *(Smiling:)* See it rhymes, eh?

COACH: ENUFF YAPPING. I WANNA SEE MORE PLAYING!

SCENE 2: THE GAME

(Fabrice flashes back to a previous game. He drops into a goalie pose and stares intensely out into the crowd.)

FABRICE: So it was the last game, eh. We were going to the finals. And it was tied four four. But we were playing against Shelly's team, The Falcons. She hadn't scored so I kinda felt bad for her, eh. She usually scores two. She's that good.

(In hockey gear, a confident 12-year-old SHELLY appears. She speaks to the audience in a normal Canadian accent and never directly to Fabrice unless noted.)

So I'm thinking...I need to win the game for da team, but dere's Shelly looking at me. She's all sad and stuff. I can see it in her eyes. They are telling me.

SHELLY: *(Faux sweetness:)* Let a softie in, Fabrice. You know you want to...

FABRICE: A softie is a goal that you should save. I never let a softie in...well except for that one time, but that wasn't my fault, eh. I lost my stick! *(Back to being hyper:)* So anyways, Shelly's eyes were talking to me and stuff and telling me what to do...

(Shelly tries to distract Fabrice with her pouting.)

But my coach was yelling at me to stay focused. Cause sometimes I start thinking about the next game that I forget I'm playing this game. I'm sure when I'm pro this won't happen — because I be like — tinking about the money I'll be making and that will keep me happy, y'know...

(WHISTLE blows. Fabrice relaxes.)

Coach calls a time out, eh.

FABRICE: He tells everybody where to go, but I'm sure nobody understands because once you get the puck you just want to skate as fast as you can and shoot. Hockey is like that. You don't think— you just do.

COACH: TIME OUT!!! *(Pause.)* You here. You— protect the point. You— clear the crease.

FABRICE: So I *sees* their coach puts Shelly out onto the ice and everything. And I tell my coach to make sure she doesn't get the puck, but he can't hear so good. He's got one ear that's bad so he just stares at me and nods.

(WHISTLE blows. He squats into goalie position.)

When the ref drops the puck, I get nervous, eh. Cause this is a big game and Shelly is on the ice. It's not good cuz I'm sure Shelly will get pissed off if I don't let her score and she's my oldest friend since I moved here from Gaspé. *(Breaking out of goalie pose:)* That's in Quebec! Y'know...da French part of Canada...the best part! See, I had no friends, eh. Nobody would talk to me cause I don't speak English no good. She was the only one that said hi. *(Approaching Shelly:)* Salut!

SHELLY: You're weird.

FABRICE: I know. I'm French.

SHELLY: No, you're just weird... But I like that. *(Pointing at his hockey logo:)* You play hockey?

FABRICE: *(Slightly defensive:)* Ya, I play goal. I'm the best!

SHELLY: I was just asking—no need to get mad... Hey, you wanna go to my birthday party? I'll introduce you to my hockey team.

FABRICE: *(To audience:)* And that's how we became friends. *(Inches closer:)* The reason I'm talking to you is because of what happened at the game... I need your opinion.

SCENE 3: TWO MINUTES FOR UNSPORTSMANLIKE CONDUCT

(Shelly mimes the following as Fabrice drops into goalie position and speaks.)

FABRICE: Shelly was racing down the sideboards. Nobody skates as fast as her in peewee. She took figure skating since she was like six so she was good and stuff. With the puck, she blows by McGruff and Jay Jay. They are our best D men.

(SLAPSHOT sound.)

But the puck wasn't completely flat when she shot it so it was wobbling and stuff. I can see it. I can save it. Cuz I'm like the best, eh? But in my brain, someting was saying "let it go...let it go" *(Standing up:)* Well, it says it in French, but I translated it for you. Would you let it by for your friend? My brain was arguing in my head! It was saying. *(Dropping into position:)* Save—you want to be a pro player. Pro players do not let softies in. No way! *(Fakes a save:)* Goal—their goalie was no good and let in four goals that period so I was sure we'd score another. The four goals on me were all accidents! *(Beat.)* I saw all of dis in my head and thought I had to save it. The game was tied. We lose! No go to finals! I had to do it for my team. There were eighteen of them and only one of her. I no want eighteen guys angry at me. Besides, Shelly would say it's just a game. She'd forgive me.

(Shelly shakes her head and gives him "thumbs down." Fabrice makes a save. Crowd ROARS!)

COACH: GREAT SAVE, FABRICE!

FABRICE: *(Bowing:)* Thank you. Thank you.

(Fabrice gently taps his stick on Shelly's leg.)

Nice shot, Shelly.

(Shelly responds by angrily "two-handed slashing" him. A WHISTLE blows. They exit.)

ACT II: INTRODUCING SHELLY

SCENE 1: THE SHOOTER

(Shelly alone, in her hockey gear.)

SHELLY: So I have this French friend, Fabrice. He's not really French, he's from Quebec... He's a real piece of work. *(As if talking to somebody who doesn't understand:)* Meaning, he's kinda hard to convince to do the right thing. He's stubborn. I mean, I'm a girl, but I'm like the best forward in the whole league. And Fabrice is the best goalie. We made each other. *(Pause.)* Now you're probably asking...what is a girl doing in a boys' hockey league? Pffft. I'm so much better than most of them — they had to let me play. Everybody loves a winner, right?

(Fabrice re-enters and squats in front of an imaginary net.)

FABRICE: I dare you to score on me!

(Shelly fires pucks at him.)

I'm unstoppable!

SHELLY: So he likes to think. He's not all that.

FABRICE: I got the technique! I got the style! Giv-er your best shot!

(Shelly fires until she scores.)

Lucky one, eh? That was an accident.

(Fabrice leaves.)

SHELLY: See, he thinks he's better than Patrick Roy or some other French goalie. Whatever. I let him think that because goalies are hard to find—nobody wants pucks slapped into their face. *(Shrugging:)* And I needed somebody to practice with.

SCENE 2: THE GAME

(Shelly flashes back to the previous game against Fabrice.)

SHELLY: So last game. Our team needed to beat Fabrice's stupid team to head to the finals. The score was tied four-four. I hadn't scored since Fabrice's team was double and triple teaming me. But I knew it would eventually happen. I always score.

(Fabrice re-enters and squats into goalie position.)

Scouts were at the game, you know. I was going to get drafted high to a good Bantam team, I was certain...if Fabrice hadn't ruined it for me.

(Shelly slaps a puck. A repeat of Fabrice's save. Crowd ROARS!)

COACH: GREAT SAVE, FABRICE!

SHELLY: He knew I liked going five hole when the puck was wobbling. He was lucky I couldn't get a clean shot! Cuz I always score on him. His weakness is high blocker side. I always go there when I can. *(Approaching Fabrice:)* Then to make it worse, he slashes me afterwards.

(Fabrice taps his stick on Shelly and says slightly mockingly.)

FABRICE: *Nice shot, Shelly...*

SHELLY: So I had to slash him back.

(Shelly responds by "two-handed slashing" him. Fabrice "fakes" being injured by it. A WHISTLE blows.)

REFEREE: Two minutes for unsportsmanlike conduct.

SHELLY: What? He slashed me first!

REFEREE: Two minutes in the sin bin, young lady.

SHELLY: I swear I heard his teammates tell Fabrice to slash me earlier. His team is so annoying—they say stuff like "How's your boyfriend?" or "Are you gonna go home and cry if I trip you?" His coach is constantly complaining about me and the refs never call penalty when I'm hooked. Everybody hates me!... And because of my penalty, they score!

(Goal HORN roars. Crowd ROARS.)

We lose!

(Shelly exits in a huff.)

SCENE 3: POST-GAME ACCORDING TO FABRICE

(Fabrice alone.)

FABRICE: So after the game, we all like shake hands and stuff. It's to show you are a good sport.

(Shelly enters. Both mime shaking hands.)

Good game, good game, good game.

SHELLY: Good game, good game, good game.

FABRICE: *(Meets Shelly:)* I was going to apologize to Shelly for causing her to take a penalty, but she won't shake my hand.

(He offers his hand to shake and so does Shelly, but she pulls it away at the last second.)

I knew she was angry with me. I didn't need to hear it but she said it anyways.

SHELLY: *(With disdain:)* I thought you were my friend.

FABRICE: Then she left... *(To audience:)* How did I feel? *(In a goalie pose:)* I am unstoppable. I don't cry! That's for the little boys! I'm a man! Je suis Le Goalie! Shelly is the one that is wrong for not shaking my hand. That's bad sportspersonship.

COACH: HEY, FABRICE. GOOD GAME!

FABRICE: *(To offstage:)* Thanks a lot, coach! *(To audience:)* Shelly and I didn't talk after. She would sometimes call me when she heard good news, even though she knows I don't like using the phone. I hate talking on it. It's like wearing a mask underwater. And I tink I sound a bit funny, y'know. Not like Shelly. She sounds nice.

(Shelly re-enters. Fabrice and Shelly mime being on the phone.)

SHELLY: Fabrice, I heard you got a shutout.

FABRICE: Yeah, my third one this year!

SHELLY: Congratulations!

FABRICE: Thanks a lot. *(To audience:)* But today?? Nothing. It's only a game, right?

SCENE 4: POST-GAME ACCORDING TO SHELLY

(Focus on Shelly – who speaks to the audience.)

SHELLY: Do you know what really bothers me? It's how Fabrice acted after the game. We were shaking hands like you're supposed to do.

(In a post-game lineup, Fabrice shakes hands with invisible players.)

FABRICE: Good game. Good game. Good game.

SHELLY: And he wouldn't shake mine!

(Shelly offers her hand, but Fabrice pulls his away at the last second.)

So I say to him— *(With disdain:)* I thought you were my friend.

(Fabrice leaves.)

And he just walks away. What the french? Some friend he turned out to be! *(Starts off but stops:)* I didn't call him afterwards. He didn't deserve it. I hope he gets scored on lots in the finals and loses.

(She exits.)

ACT III: THE BIRTHDAY PARTIES

SCENE 1: ANNOUNCING PARTIES

(Fabrice and Shelly on opposite sides of the stage — speaking to the audience, but never to another.)

FABRICE: So Shelly was having a birthday party.

SHELLY: I was having a birthday party for my twelfth. I knew tons of boys! And of course the girls wanted to show up too.

FABRICE: She knows lots of people. I bet dere was going to be fifty kids dere. I couldn't even get five to show up to my birthday.

SHELLY: But I didn't want to invite Fabrice after what happened last game. His team beat the other team 10-0. They were total pushovers! We could have been city champs!

FABRICE: But I didn't want to go. No way!

FABRICE: *(Pointing:)* She has to apologize first!

SHELLY: *(Pointing:)* He has to apologize first!

SCENE 2: SHELLY'S PARTY

(Fabrice and Shelly swap sides.)

FABRICE: At the party. The boys stood in one area and all the girls in another — except Shelly. She was talking to the boys. I stood by myself because the boys were her teammates, y'know. They weren't going to be friendly to me. No way!

SHELLY: I was talking to the boys...and made sure Fabrice saw. I wasn't going to talk to him so I made sure he knew. I told Brandon, a winger on my team, that I was angry at Fabrice. And he went to talk to him! It wasn't my fault!

FABRICE: So one of the Shelly's teammates bumps me. Not a little bump—like oops. But a big one. Like he meant it. I says to him, "What's that for??" and he says, "You were in my way Frenchie!" *(Agitated:)* I hate being called names. It's like being spit on, eh. So I shove him back, eh. He makes a face— *(Scrunching up his own face:)*—like this and tells me to "Buzz off!"—then shoves me. *(Even more agitated:)* I hate being hit so I push him back. One ting leads to another and I accidentally *fell* onto one of Shelly's teammates. Soon we were all pushing and shoving when I hear—

SHELLY: STOP IT!

FABRICE: *(Philosophically:)* You know when the rain stops and the sun comes out. It was like that. There's supposed to be a rainbow, but there wasn't a rainbow that day.

SHELLY: Fabrice, get out of my party! I didn't want to invite you anyways! My mom made me!

FABRICE: *(Dejected:)* Oh... And I thought she was there to help me, but no. She was just like everyone else. Mean... So I left.

(He begins shuffling off, but stops.)

I don't need her! I don't need anybody! I'm unstoppable! I am Fabrice Allaire! The greatest goalie in the world!

(Finally storms off.)

SHELLY: At first, I was so glad Fabrice left. What a total downer. He was ruining my party! Then my mom yelled at me. Told me I had to apologize. "For what?" I said. She said I showed bad judgment. Tell that to Fabrice! He started it! I thought he was my friend!

SCENE 3: FABRICE'S PARTY

(Again, Fabrice and Shelly at opposite ends of the stage.)

FABRICE: So a week later, I had my birthday party. I made sure I wasn't gonna invite nobody I didn't like.

SHELLY: So a week later, Fabrice had his birthday party.

FABRICE: My mom made me invite her.

SHELLY: My mom made me go.

FABRICE: I didn't want to!

SHELLY: I didn't want to! Mom said it was "a good opportunity to make amends." *(Rolling her eyes:)* Whatever that means.

FABRICE: The whole team was at my house. It was great. First time I felt so popular... I guess my mom talked to all the other parents cause I know some of my teammates don't like me and they were there. And it was the first time we saw each other since the finals. *(Bragging:)* I got a shutout by the way. I'm going pro.

SHELLY: So Fabrice invited his entire team to his party. It was lame. No one there was his real friend...they just played hockey with him. Okay, maybe Maurice and that's because Maurice had a French name and his grandparents were from Quebec.

FABRICE: So Shelly was the only girl at the party. She probably felt pretty weird. That was good because I wanted her to.

SHELLY: Did I tell you I was the only girl. Hello? I stick out. I was wearing a dress too cuz my mom made me. But I'm sure I could beat up most of Fabrice's teammates though. That's how tough I am. And I'm still a girl.

FABRICE: I was having a good time. Everyone was wishing "Happy Birthday" to me...except for one person.

(He glances over to Shelly. She gives him a disgusted look.)

SHELLY: He had all his friends around him. I wanted to at least say hi and maybe listen to his apology. But he's stubborn and I'm sure if he did it would because of his mom. He's a mama's boy.

FABRICE: Mom nudges me, eh. She says I should talk to Shelly, but I say later. She knows we had a fight after the game... Moms know everyting—even if you don't tell them. They got Mom-radar. When you sleep your dreams your secrets leak out and travel over to your Mom and tell them things. It's true.

SHELLY: I heard from Stan who heard from Kevin...that Fabrice was looking to apologize. Finally!

FABRICE: I heard from Kevin who heard from Trey that Shelly wanted to say sorry... Good!

(Fabrice struts over to Shelly.)

SHELLY: So Fabrice walks up to me—looking all angry and stuff. I don't want to talk to an angry midget.

(Shelly turns to face Fabrice. She's not happy.)

FABRICE: She looks mad at me. So I just stand next to her. I'm waiting and waiting...but she doesn't say anything, eh.

SHELLY: I decide to mess with his head. I start opening and closing my mouth like I'm talking, but say nothing.

(Shelly mouths words without saying anything.)

FABRICE: She starts doing a fish thing with her mouth. I had no idea what she was thinking. Girls are weird. So I start copying her, eh.

(Fabrice mouths words without saying anything.)

SHELLY: Then he starts mimicking me. What the french? I hate when people do that—don't you? Fabrice knows this is my pet peeve. And this is exactly why I'm not friends with him anymore!

FABRICE: Before she can say sorry, my friend Jordan bumps into her. I didn't want him to do it. He says her to—

JORDAN: Why are you still around, girly?

FABRICE: He hates it when a girl plays better than him. He's pretty fast and can shoot, but Shelly's much better. Jordan bumps her again for no reason and that's when Shelly punches him in the gut. I grab him before he can jump her. Then I yell at her.

SHELLY: Fabrice tells me to get out! Fine, I say...it's your stupid party and I didn't want to come anyways!

(Shelly storms out.)

FABRICE: No way could Shelly handle ten angry boys. I had to tell her to get out. She would have gotten into a more trouble if she stayed. Jordan is a real bad guy. He doesn't understand the word stop. After Shelly leaves, I tell Jordan he's not welcome anymore. He doesn't say anything, but gives me an angry look. I know that look... I see it all the time.

(Fabrice walks off.)

SCENE 4: MAKING AMENDS

(Shelly reappears – a little teary.)

SHELLY: Stoopid Fabrice made me cry. It's all his fault. I told Mom what happened and she said I should probably stop playing hockey if I got into all this drama. She said she was going to call Fabrice and yell at his mother for letting her son kick me out. Stoopid Fabrice. I hate him so much right now.

(Fabrice reappears.)

FABRICE: So after what happened, I thought I should call Shelly or her mother to tell her it wasn't her fault and that it was all Jordan. I only said those things to protect her.

SHELLY: So Mom calls Fabrice's mom, but instead of getting angry at Fabrice—she's angry at me. What did I do? She says I need to speak to him A-S-A-P.

(Both of them pick up imaginary phones simultaneously.)

FABRICE: *(Calling on phone:)* Hello?   **SHELLY:** *(Calling on phone:)* Hello?

FABRICE: It's busy...

SHELLY: The line is busy...

FABRICE: Guess she doesn't want to talk to me.

SHELLY: Guess he still hates me.

(Fabrice walks off. Shelly starts off.)

Wait...it could be busy because of his mother. She's always on the phone talking! I'll try again.

(She dials.)

It's ringing.

FABRICE: Hello?

SHELLY: Hey.

FABRICE: Shelly?

SHELLY: Yeah?

FABRICE: You ready to apologize?

SHELLY: *(Incredulous:)* Are you?

(Long silence. They speak almost simultaneously.)

FABRICE: You first. I'm sorry. Me too.   **SHELLY:** You first. I'm sorry. Me too

(They exit.)

SCENE 5: LE GOALIE

(Fabrice and Shelly return in hockey gear and holding their sticks. Fabrice goes into his goalie stance.)

FABRICE: I can stop anyting. I got the technique! I got the style! I am unstoppable! I'm the best since Patrick Roy. Better than Marc Andre Fleury. Better than that JS Giguere guy. Oh, you need just one more goal? Well too bad eh! *(Realizing what's he said:)* I'm sorry, I didn't mean that against you.

SHELLY: No worries... I can score on you any time.

(She shoots and scores [he lets it go in]. She raises her arms in celebration! Goal HORN sounds.)

FABRICE: That was lucky. You were distracting me! I call redo.

(They go back to playing hockey. Lights down. The end.)

The Author Speaks

What inspired you to write this play?
Some of my best friends I made as a kid—I met playing team sports. There's something about the act of playing together that breaks down cultural and socio-economic barriers for a few hours. I was the weird new kid on the block who didn't know anybody nor have the courage to speak up—but through street hockey I met every young person in my block and learnt the game that I love today. This camaraderie is why youth sports is so important to our culture. But when sports become more about competition than camaraderie then "sports is war" rears its ugly head. And in war, nobody wins. Theatre is like sports. It's as vital to young people in society and must be supported. There is something about the emotional expression of the self that is just as important as physical exercise to the body. And like sports, through the pain and joy of performing live theatre, friends are made and memories of a lifetime are formed. And so, two of my favourite things were melded together to form *Le Goalie*. I hope you enjoy reading it as I did writing it.

Was the structure of the play influenced by any other work?
Le Goalie is a "he-said, she-said" alternating point-of-view tale that utilizes a technique called the Rashomon-effect named after the Akira Kurosawa film in which multiple characters tell conflicting and often disturbing stories about the same event— leaving the audience wondering who is telling the truth and is that the version we want to believe?

Have you dealt with the same theme in other works that you have written?
As a playwright, I write stories that are part fantasy, part reality. In real life, I played often against a female pitcher in little league, but I was never a star player like Fabrice—that's the fantasy part! Since my tales are loosely based on my experiences and/or beliefs, there are recurring themes. One of

them is that the nature of truth is slippery because humans colour their experiences by their personal viewpoints of the world. Without diving into philosophy and moral relativism, I only want to say I like my characters complex with many internal conflicts. My characters will outright lie—but for valid reasons: to get something, to protect their ego, to protect someone else. Rarely will my characters be good honest folk (nothing wrong with them—I admire them in real life). It just makes them less interesting and thus creates a less interesting story. To me, great stories are about relationships. Bad stories are about conflict.

What writers have had the most profound effect on your style?
When I first began writing, I emulated popular modern writers thinking "if they were famous why couldn't I be?" And so, I copied the quirky metafictional (a word meaning the author speaks directly to you, but not really because his cell phone bill would be astronomical chatting to every reader) style of Lemony Snicket and his macabre humour. Although it was misguided, I learnt the craft of writing and storytelling through it. By actively practicing (not dreaming) to be some other writer, I learnt the construction of narratives and literary styles. I encourage copying as training as it's akin to playing a song or drawing in another artist's style. There is no better teacher than practice. Eventually, I settled into my own style and created tales based on my own experiences and viewpoints, not others. To name a few influential writers to me—John Mighton for his incredible ability to seamlessly integrate modern topics (science and math) into theatre with everyday characters, Louis Sachar for his absurd but realistic and engaging characters, and Lin Manuel Miranda and Cole Porter for being such amazing lyricists.

What are the most common mistakes that occur in productions of your work?
The lack of physical action when characters are speaking. I call

it talking head syndrome. In my plays, I attempt to create active characters who have strong wants and desires — and while I write the dialogue I only hint at everything else: the set, costumes, and actions. Those bits are as important as the text, as the text is a blueprint and a blueprint does not a house make. Thousands of other decisions are required — so feel free to build that dome house out of gingerbread. I encourage it.

What inspired you to become a playwright?
When I first saw *Honus & Me* (play by Steven Dietz, novel by Dan Gutman) on stage. It was magic. Everybody laughed, cried, and went awwwwe at the right times. A *Field of Dreams* for all ages. I said to myself, forget novels — this is where greatness happens...live theatre!

Are any characters modeled after real life or historical figures?
Fabrice is modeled after Quebecois netminders like Patrick Roy and Canada's former French-speaking prime minister, Jean Chretien. The Quebecois English accent is very rhythmic and recognizable.

Do any films/videos exist of prior productions of this play?
If there was a mind camera there would be. Trust me your mind would be blown too. It blew mine.

Shakespeare gave advice to the players in *Hamlet*; if you could give advice to your cast what would it be?
Make bold choices. Don't act, just be. If you believe in the character, so will the audience. Also wear socks. There's nothing in this world worse than stinky feet.

About the Author

Nelson Yu is a Toronto-based playwright, screenwriter, middle-grade novelist, and video game developer. His plays and musicals have been produced in Canada. He studied under acclaimed MG/YA author Richard Scrimger at the

Humber School for Writers and acting & writing at George Brown College and Second City Toronto. He is a graduate of the University of Toronto (BSc) and Humber College's Creative Writing program.

MATH-O-FREAK

A short comedy by
Nancy Brewka-Clark

CAST OF CHARACTERS

LIBBY, a girl dance student.

KIRK, a boy math whiz.

ROBIN, a girl dance student.

SETTING

The school bus stop.

TIME

The present.

(LIBBY and KIRK are waiting for the bus.)

LIBBY: Why doesn't the stupid bus come?

KIRK: It's merely a matter of fixed spatial objects versus moving objects and the velocity at which —

LIBBY: Don't let Robin Miller hear you talking like that. It's just, just — geeky.

KIRK: *(Laughs.)* You're not jealous, are you?

(Libby stares at him icily.)

LIBBY: And why would I be jealous?

KIRK: *(Shrugs:)* I don't know.

LIBBY: *(Offhand, craning stage left for bus again:)* You must know. You said it.

KIRK: I mean, it's just logical. You like me and I like you, but I like Robin, too. *(He strokes chin, narrowing eyes:)* Uh-oh. Now there's a formula for trouble.

LIBBY: No it isn't. You and I have been friends from birth. Robin just moved here, so she can't ever be your friend from birth.

KIRK: When you put it that way —

LIBBY: Yeah, I know. It's logical. *(Waves stage right:)* Look! Here she comes now.

KIRK: No way. Her dad drives her to school.

LIBBY: Her dad's away on business. He's in Japan. When he comes back he's bringing her a string of pearls, real ones. Hi, Robin!

(ROBIN enters stage right.)

ROBIN: Hi, Libby.

KIRK: Hi, Libby.

(Libby and Robin both stare at him.)

What?

LIBBY: You said, "Hi, Libby."

KIRK: No, I didn't.

LIBBY: Yes, you did.

KIRK: Well, what I meant was, "Hi, Lobbin." *(He smacks himself on forehead.)* I mean Robin.

ROBIN: Hi. *(She rolls eyes, turns immediately to Libby.)* Are you trying out for *The Nutcracker?*

KIRK: Nutcracker? How can you try out to be a nutcracker?

(Once more Libby and Robin stare at him.)

It's a kitchen utensil. How can you try out to be a kitchen utensil?

LIBBY: It's a ballet.

ROBIN: It's famous. People have been performing it for more than one hundred years.

KIRK: Oh, that *Nutcracker.* *(He waves his arms.)* It's all about how they save this walnut from the clutches of an evil metal tool, right? *(He speaks in high pitch:)* "Leave me alone, you nasty nutcracker, or I'll roll away under the table where you'll never find me." *(He deepens voice:)* "Walnut, you crack me up."

LIBBY: Not exactly. It's about this girl, Clara, and how on Christmas Eve all her toys come to life and dance.

ROBIN: And there's a beautiful fairy, the Sugarplum, and dancing snowflakes, and flowers.

KIRK: Girl stuff. No wonder I've never heard of it—oops, I mean—

ROBIN: Don't worry, Kirk, we knew that already. And it isn't just girl stuff. The nutcracker is really a handsome prince and he has this huge battle with the wicked mouse king.

LIBBY: And Clara kills the mouse king by hitting him in the head with her shoe.

KIRK: Sounds like the nutcracker's a wimp.

LIBBY: He's—oh, never mind, you wouldn't get it anyway.

KIRK: True. Because it's girl stuff.

ROBIN: Madame Dumont—she's our ballet teacher—says that in a typical workout the biggest, toughest, strongest football player couldn't keep up with a ballerina.

KIRK: Then why aren't there ballerinas in Super Bowls?

(Libby and Robin exchange a knowing look and laugh.)

LIBBY: Kirk, have you ever heard of Lynn Swann?

KIRK: Ah hah! You're trying to trick me, aren't you? But, I'm too smart for that, oh, yeah. You see, girls, I happen to know that there's a ballet by that name.

LIBBY: *(Gaping at him:)* There's a ballet called "Lynn Swann"?

KIRK: Oh, so you don't know about it, huh?

ROBIN: Uh, Kirk, it's *Swan Lake*.

KIRK: What is?

ROBIN: *(With big sigh:)* The ballet you're thinking of—it's by Mr. Peter Ilyich Tchaikovsky. And it's famous, too.

LIBBY: Oh, Kirk, don't feel bad. After all, math-o-freaks aren't supposed to know anything about anything except numbers, numbers, and more numbers.

ROBIN: *(Another big sigh:)* So, do you know who Lynn Swann is or not?

KIRK: *(Mocking her big sigh:)* I can see you're just dying to tell me. So tell me.

LIBBY: He played for the Pittsburgh Steelers back in the 1970s.

ROBIN: He played in four Super Bowls. And he was a dancer. A ballet dancer.

KIRK: Are you sure about this?

LIBBY: Of course we're sure. He studied dance all the way through school, even in college. That's why he played so well. He wasn't just strong, he was graceful.

KIRK: A ballet dancer can't be stronger than a football player. It's not—

LIBBY: *(Puts hands over ears:)* Don't say it.

KIRK: *(Loudly:)* Logical.

ROBIN: Well, you're right. It's not.

KIRK: At least somebody around here can put one and one together and come up with two.

ROBIN: What I mean is pound for pound logically there's no way a ballet dancer could tackle a football player and knock him down.

KIRK: At least somebody around here can see what's logical.

ROBIN: But Madame Dumont says ballet dancers use muscles that football players don't even know they have.

LIBBY: Even the foot movements you learn when you first start are harder than you'd ever believe.

KIRK: *(He puts out a straight leg and waggles his foot.)* Boy, you're right, that was hard. I wonder if I have the strength to do that again? *(Repeats move:)* Man, I'm so tired now I might have to lie down and take a nap. *(He flops onto ground.)* Wake me up when the bus comes, okay?

(He shuts his eyes and snores.)

LIBBY: *(She prods Kirk with her toe:)* Get up or we'll dance right over you when the bus comes.

KIRK: *(Gets up.)* I'd like to see that.

LIBBY: So, you want us to dance?

KIRK: Unless you want to score a touchdown or something.

ROBIN: Okay, we'll dance.

(Robin turns Libby in a pirouette.)

KIRK: *(Applauding:)* I've never seen anything so lovely. Why, you're as graceful as football players.

LIBBY: Oh, what do you know about it, you math-o-freak?

KIRK: Quite a bit, actually. *(He strokes chin, nodding:)* Torque.

LIBBY & ROBIN: What?

KIRK: You just did a perfect demonstration of torque.

LIBBY: *(To Robin:)* Well, at least he said it was perfect, whatever it is.

KIRK: Welcome to my world! What you just did was a perfect example of torque, or, to put it another way, the propensity of an object to turn after force is applied to it. In this case, you rotated, or, to put it another way, you pivoted.

ROBIN: Actually, it's called a pirouette.

(Robin and Libby pirouette again.)

And we're not using force. What do you think this is, football?

KIRK: Here's the parallel. Designing football plays is like creating ballet moves. The coach uses a series of mathematical formulas to propel his objects in patterns.

LIBBY: I wonder what Madame Dumont would say if she heard you calling a dancer an object.

ROBIN: *(Laughs:)* I bet she'd object.

LIBBY: We could find out.

ROBIN: Kirk, why don't you come to the next dance class with us?

LIBBY: If you start taking dance lessons now, by the time you're out of college you can play the nutcracker.

KIRK: *(Looks back and forth between them:)* Who says I can't right now?

(He jumps, spins, falls. Libby and Robin help him up.)

LIBBY: Better work on your torque first.

(Blackout. The end.)

The Author Speaks

What inspired you to write this play?
Occasionally I run kids' classes at The Shipbuilding Museum in Essex, MA, where the focus is on the men who built the great wooden schooners and sailed them, often at great risk. And of course the focus is on tools and charts and measurements. One of the exhibits shows all the houses around town where all the "fittings" for the vessels and the crew were made. When I ask the kids what they think the women are doing when they make "fittings," I invariably get a lot of sassy answers from the boys. This is when I deliver the great revelation: math and science are part of everyday life for both genders and always have been. Try cutting a piece of sailcloth without measuring it and see how far you get! Everything from baking hardtack to pickling fish to weaving a blanket involves math and science. *Math-O-Freak* has fun with exploding modern gender stereotypes: Kirk considers himself a mathematical genius, but he's a good enough sport to laugh at himself when Libby and Robin outwit him from every angle. And since they do it while laughing at themselves, everybody's happy.

Was the structure of the play influenced by any other work?
I think the "waiting for" theme that Samuel Beckett employed so famously is always bursting with possibilities: how many things can happen to you while you're waiting for the bus? In a very short time, Kirk almost loses a friend only to gain two dance partners. When you think about it, lots of things happen to people in plays when they appear to be just hanging around: the guys are just chatting up there on the parapet when the ghost of Hamlet's father groans and the tragedy unreels. In the case of *Math-O-Freak*, Kirk, Libby and Robin aren't the kind of kids to waste time while they're waiting either. Sports, ballet, mathematical formulas—in just a few

minutes the girls reveal a link that literally sends Kirk reeling.

Have you dealt with the same theme in other works that you have written?
I've been a mystery writer and a member of Sisters in Crime for a long time. The crucial element in a mystery is the tantalizing wait for a solution. The first mystery I had published was a short story in *The Boston Globe* Sunday magazine in 1983, in which a young man thinks he's going to achieve immortality with a single poem. The plot flows along on an intellectual level and then—bang! In another short mystery, I have the reader waiting for the bang! that never comes. I guess you could call that the Godot approach to waiting. In *Math-O-Freak*, the questions get answered by the time the bus comes.

What writers have had the most profound effect on your style?
As a kid, I was fascinated when I saw some early black and white clips from the TV comedy writer Ernie Kovacs. His short comedy routines combined a blend of sophistication and downright strangeness that I think have kept generations of script writers inspired. Carl Reiner and Lucille Ball and Carol Burnett and Mel Brooks and Woody Allen all provided great laughs when I was growing up. I admire writers who can produce serious drama immensely, and yet for me, it's important to have my young actors get their audiences to laugh. In *Math-O-Freak* the humor comes from reversing gender stereotypes, which can still hamper kids from reaching their full potential.

What do you hope to achieve with this work?
Math-O-Freak debunks the concepts that boys are good at sports and girls are good at the performing arts and never the twain shall meet. When you actually think about it, they're pretty much the same. In this case, the plot has a twist—or

should I say torque? Well, that's the word Kirk uses. As for Libby and Robin, they prefer to say pirouette. And when you throw in a swan—actually a Swann, as in Super Bowl hero—the play becomes Emily Dickinson's phrase for hope: the "thing with feathers."

What inspired you to become a playwright?

I started writing dialogue way back in college. I forced myself to act as well on the theory that you shouldn't write for other people without knowing what it feels like to be up there with someone else's words in your mouth. But I often forgot entire chunks of dialogue (see above) from sheer terror so I knew the public life was not for me. I had always planned to be a writer but couldn't imagine boxing myself in with a particular genre. So, for a long time I was a nonfiction writer and editor who wrote romances and poetry on the side. For two decades I was also heavily into a type of 18th-century painting called japanning, which I combined with Russian folk patterns, and did commercial work including a spring ad campaign for Colombian coffee that ran in almost every magazine in the U.S. and Europe. However, by the late 1990s I was back in the groove of writing full time. I went back to writing drama with a passion after I wrote a full-length comedy about President William Howard Taft's Summer White House in Beverly, MA, where I live, as a fundraiser to kick off a multimillion-dollar restoration project sponsored by the City of Beverly. I also wrote four children's plays as adjuncts to the main play and realized I loved writing for kids. We went on to use those productions for five years until in 2002 I rewrote the main play to incorporate the kids' themes. And that in turn inspired me to do more kids' plays.

How did you research the subject?

It's amazing how even the simplest things require research. When I started writing the play I hadn't consciously made the connection between the ballet *Swan Lake* and the football player Lynn Swann. But when Libby and Robin start to educate Kirk about how hard ballet dancers work to maintain their athleticism without looking clumsy, they bring up the name — not me! Then I had to look up exactly who he was and when he played so that the girls could in turn explain it all to Kirk. Serendipitous things like that always make me laugh. And hopefully the audience will, too.

Are any characters modeled after real life or historical figures?
I think it would probably amaze a four-time Super Bowl champ that his name is being invoked by two ballet students, but in my opinion, more people should know about Lynn Swann's dance training. The premise of **Math-O-Freak** is to expand a young student's horizons in keeping with current attitudes toward fitness: more men are doing yoga and more women work out with weights. The point of the play is to make kids feel at home in their own bodies no matter what kind of physical activity they take up. To go back to that shipbuilding museum for a moment, I love telling kids that men back then were terrific knitters and superstars with a needle and thread. And when it comes to bling, show me anybody, male or female, who wouldn't want four Super Bowl rings!

Shakespeare gave advice to the players in *Hamlet*; if you could give advice to your cast what would it be?
I think one of the funniest expressions is: act natural. It's the kind of thing an adult says without really thinking about it. But what I love about working with kids is that they pick up on contradictions. Another funny one is: be yourself. Since I admire more than anything people of any age who can memorize lines and lines of someone else's thoughts and then say them with conviction, I'd simply say, "Thank you for

bringing my words to life."

About the Author

A professional writer for four decades, **Nancy Brewka-Clark** began her career after graduating from Wheaton College by covering Boston theater for many newspapers and magazines, interviewing luminaries such as legendary queen of the Yiddish theatre Molly Picon, Douglas Fairbanks, Jr., Jane Powell, Leonard Nimoy, Sandy Dennis, Robert Brustein and Israel Horovitz. It wasn't until 1997 that she wrote her first ten-minute comedy for a Boston competition to be judged by Craig Lucas. Although an April ice storm prevented both her and him from actually seeing the performance, her determination was fixed: she would think big and write small. Since then, her plays have been produced in venues as varied as Brooklyn, New York, and Harrogate, England, and many of her comic monologues have been published by Smith and Kraus.

BRACE YOURSELF

A short comedy by
Keegon Schuett

CAST OF CHARACTERS

MIRANDA, a young girl with braces.

TOMMY, a normal guy.

LUCY, a good friend.

CRAIG, a dependable bro.

(Two girls, LUCY and MIRANDA, sit together outside during lunch. Across the stage sitting together are two boys, CRAIG and TOMMY.)

MIRANDA: This is the worst day of my entire life.

LUCY: No! No, today's a big day. It's what—two months now? He's going to ask you—

MIRANDA: He can't see me like this. You have to tell him he can't see me like this.

LUCY: They're just braces, Miranda. You're still very pretty.

MIRANDA: That's exactly what you'd say if I wasn't pretty anymore because of my braces.

LUCY: That's not true.

MIRANDA: Yes, it is and he's going to think so, too.

LUCY: You are pretty. Now you've just got a shinier smile. And besides—

MIRANDA: Don't. Don't tell me that Tommy loves me for my inner beauty. Don't say that. That's cheesy.

LUCY: That's not what I was going to say...but he probably does.

MIRANDA: Probably...it has been two months.

LUCY: Big anniversary. He's definitely going to ask you to the dance, Miranda.

MIRANDA: Not now. Now I'm half metal. I've got robot teeth. He's going to dump me as soon as he finds out.

LUCY: Well, what do you want to do? He's waiting for you.

MIRANDA: I want to die. I want to be invisible. Hand me the mirror.

LUCY: No. You're obsessing.

MIRANDA: Mirror. Now.

LUCY: Fine.

(She passes her a small mirror. Miranda observes her braces up close, very upset. Craig approaches Lucy.)

CRAIG: Hey, Lucy. Over here.

(Lucy walks to him.)

LUCY: What's up?

CRAIG: Tommy's been looking for Miranda. He wants to talk to her.

LUCY: The dance, right?

CRAIG: Probably. It's been a while.

LUCY: Two month anniversary. Huge.

CRAIG: I think he's got something special planned. Could you send her over?

LUCY: No. I can't.

CRAIG: Why not?

LUCY: It's complicated, Craig.

CRAIG: Well, what should I tell him? He's waiting.

LUCY: I don't know. Tell him she doesn't want to see him.

CRAIG: Anymore?

LUCY: No. She doesn't want to see him.

CRAIG: Wow. OK. Thanks, I guess.

LUCY: No problem.

(Craig goes to Tommy.)

TOMMY: She coming?

CRAIG: Uhh, I don't think so, bro.

TOMMY: Why not?

CRAIG: Lucy said that she said she doesn't want to see you anymore.

TOMMY: At all?

CRAIG: Yeah, that's the way it sounded, man. I'm sorry.

TOMMY: I thought she liked me.

CRAIG: Girls are like that. One minute they love you. Next minute they dump you through a friend, I guess.

TOMMY: I planned this whole thing.

CRAIG: I know. Tough break.

LUCY: *(To Miranda:)* Stop looking in the mirror.

MIRANDA: No. Not until I get used to the glare.

LUCY: Nobody's glaring.

MIRANDA: I meant the way my mouth reflects sun now. Are people staring?

LUCY: No one's looking over here. Tommy was looking for you, though.

MIRANDA: What? What'd you say?

LUCY: The truth.

MIRANDA: No! You didn't tell him about the —

LUCY: I just said that you didn't want to see him.

TOMMY: *(To Craig:)* I made her this necklace with lettered beads. It says, "Will you go to the dance with me, Miranda?"

CRAIG: That's a lot of beads.

MIRANDA: *(To Lucy:)* But I do want to see him. I just don't want him to see me like this.

LUCY: Do you want me to go get him? He'll understand, Miranda. He likes you.

MIRANDA: Oh, God. Uhh, yes. Go tell him I want to see him. Go before I change my mind.

(Lucy walks to Tommy and Craig.)

TOMMY: It's a pretty big necklace. And I was planning on kissing her.

CRAIG: You guys hadn't kissed?

TOMMY: No. And now we can't. We'll never kiss. Never.

(Lucy only catches the end of his sentence. She gasps and quickly returns to Miranda.)

MIRANDA: So?

LUCY: Nothing!

MIRANDA: Nothing?

LUCY: I can't say. Don't worry. It's nothing.

MIRANDA: You're freaking me out, Lucy. What did he say?

LUCY: Don't be mad if I tell you.

MIRANDA: I'm going to be mad if you don't tell me.

LUCY: OK, don't freak out, but I just heard Tommy tell Craig that he's never going to kiss you.

MIRANDA: Never?

LUCY: That's what he said.

MIRANDA: Oh, God. Oh, no! He must have heard about the braces!

LUCY: No! Maybe, but—

MIRANDA: You don't think he wants to see me so he can dump me, do you? Oh my God, he wants to break up.

LUCY: I wish I hadn't heard anything.

MIRANDA: Two months of true love down the drain because my teeth are too crooked.

LUCY: Look on the bright side.

MIRANDA: What's that?

LUCY: Your teeth won't be crooked after the braces come off.

MIRANDA: That's the best you can do? I'm a metal-mouthed monster and now I'm single! I'm gonna die alone! All alone!

(She begins to sob.)

CRAIG: It's not too late, bro. Go talk to her. Convince her that you're still the right dude for her.

TOMMY: You think there's some other dude?

CRAIG: No, bro. No. I'm just saying you need to assert yourself. You want her for another two months, you gotta tell her.

LUCY: *(To Miranda:)* Stop crying! It's not the end of the world. You can win him back.

MIRANDA: How?

LUCY: Own those teeth. He didn't fall in love with you for your mouth. He loves you because of who you are, Miranda. Go tell him what's up.

CRAIG: *(To Tommy:)* You go give her that necklace and she'll give you her heart.

TOMMY: That's poetic.

CRAIG: I know. Now go get her, tiger.

MIRANDA: *(To Lucy:)* You're right. I'm beautiful.

LUCY: You're a catch.

MIRANDA: *(Hyperventilating:)* I'm a catch! I'm not a monster...I'm worthwhile. I'm great. I'm a catch.

LUCY: Hey, hey. Catch your breath.

MIRANDA: I'm freaking out.

LUCY: Go tell him. You'll feel better after you do. Just go.

MIRANDA: Here goes nothing.

TOMMY: Here goes nothing.

(Miranda and Tommy meet at center.)

We need to talk.

MIRANDA: Stop. Don't break up with me.

TOMMY: Break up with you? I thought you—

MIRANDA: Look, I know you heard about my braces. I know you don't ever want to kiss me. And I just want to change your mind.

TOMMY: You got braces?

MIRANDA: I get it, OK? I get it! I've got more metal in my mouth than a bird cage. I've got more metal in my mouth than a skyscraper. All of that may be true, but all I know is these past two months have really meant a lot to me and I thought I was more to you than a pretty smile.

TOMMY: Miranda, I don't want to break up with you.

MIRANDA: I'm a lot more than a mouth full of braces, OK? I'm a smart girl. I'm a pretty girl. I've got a good sense of humor. I'm most of the whole package. And if you can't accept that then I'm better off without you.

TOMMY: Miranda! I don't want to break up!

MIRANDA: You don't?

TOMMY: I thought you wanted to break up with me.

MIRANDA: What? Why?

TOMMY: Lucy told Craig that you said you didn't want to see me anymore.

MIRANDA: No! I just didn't want you to see me like this.

TOMMY: Like what?

MIRANDA: With braces.

TOMMY: Why would I care if you had braces? I think you look great.

MIRANDA: You do?

TOMMY: I like your mouth full of bling.

MIRANDA: Stop it. You really don't mind them?

TOMMY: You look better than ever.

MIRANDA: Really?

TOMMY: Really.

(She smiles.)

I've got just the thing to go with your bling.

MIRANDA: What's that?

(He pulls out a big, clumsy necklace with a lot of beads.)

TOMMY: Here.

MIRANDA: Whoa, that's a lot of beads.

TOMMY: Read it.

MIRANDA: "Will you go to the dance—" YES! Definitely!

(She throws the necklace on and looks back to Lucy, pointing at the necklace.)

He asked me!

LUCY: Told ya so!

TOMMY: *(To Miranda:)* You will?

MIRANDA: Yes! A thousand times, yes!

TOMMY: *(To Craig:)* She said yes!

CRAIG: You go, bro!

TOMMY: *(To Miranda:)* Happy two month anniversary, Miranda!

(Miranda smiles. Tommy kisses her on the cheek. Blackout. End of play.)

The Author Speaks

What inspired you to write this play?

When writing for young actors, I frequently pull from my own middle and high school experiences, which weren't too terribly long ago. As a teenager going into my first year of high school, I had to wear braces to fix my teeth and straighten my smile. It was a difficult transition for me. I was already self-conscious, and the extra metal in my mouth certainly didn't do anything to help. When I had the braces it felt like they were isolating me, like I was the only one in the world who had them. My own experiences with orthodontics felt rather melodramatic, and I thought that it was a really potent topic for a short play. I really consciously wanted to write something fun and with frenetic, zany energy. I also really love plays with terrible miscommunications and misunderstandings, because I feel like they're the funniest situations in storytelling.

Was the structure or other elements of the play influenced by any other work?

I think the biggest stylistic influence on this short play is the hours of sitcom television I have watched recently. There are frequently misunderstandings and zany situations that I feel are reflected in the premise of this play. Most influential would probably be *How I Met Your Mother* or *Friends*; those shows exemplify the qualities that make sitcom television so potent and fun. It's also impossible to ignore the influence of the childhood game of Telephone, where one person says something and then it's misinterpreted through a series of people. The play follows this same principle, only it's a little bit more condensed.

Have you dealt with the same theme in other works that you have written?

I deal with the difficulty in transitioning through different phases of life in almost all of my other plays, and there is often observation about superficiality in our culture, especially the culture of younger people. Not everything is as it seems, and for children it can be complicated trying to differentiate between what's normal and abnormal. Appearances are a big part of modern life, and insecurities about image are an important thing to discuss in plays for younger actors. When I grew up, I had a really poor self-image and my self esteem was seriously lacking. This is an issue that I've worked through in many of my plays, and I hope that students struggling through similar situations can find strength in acting out these scenarios.

What writers have had the most profound effect on your style?

Lately I've found myself inspired by writers who are conscious of rhythm. I've been reading some Samuel Beckett lately and find his writing really inspirational. I'm terribly fascinated by the writing of Woody Allen and the intellectual, stunted frenzy that his dialogue is filled with. Everyone is so clever and witty, and yet so many of them are fatigued by serious insecurities and social shortcomings. I find characters like that to be interesting because their strengths are given equal weight to their weaknesses and that sort of rendering feels more real to me. While I'm ever appreciative of the fast and rapid pacing that modern writers have adopted, I also find myself particularly influenced by the poetry of the classics (especially Euripides). While that influence isn't super evident in my work, the way they utilize poetry and music in their speeches is something I strive to achieve even in small doses in my plays.

What do you hope to achieve with this work?
I hope that someone out there with braces or any other possible insecurity can be a part of this play or see this work and realize that their worth is larger than any small superficial detail of life. Confidence is an important part of life and not everyone is born with it...it's a process, something that you grow into. Don't allow others to dictate how you feel about yourself. I hope that this work can facilitate a dialogue about discovering a stronger self-image and encouraging better communication skills in our ever-changing social media landscape. If nothing else, I hope that this play can influence a smile or laugh for someone out there. Our problems can feel so much bigger and more insurmountable than they actually are, and theatre can provide an escape for people that they might not otherwise have. Facilitating a good sense of humor is an invaluable part of life, and if I can help anyone discover their strength through humor, I've achieved my goal and then some.

What were the biggest challenges involved in the writing of this play?
I had a lot of trouble figuring out the rhythm of this play. Characters speak frequently and I tried to alternate between the conversations for a more intricate and interesting experience for both the actors and the audience. I had a bit of trouble figuring out exactly what the misheard words or sentences were going to be, which is obviously a huge part of this play's success. I also had to challenge myself to remember just what it felt like to have braces, so I had to do some serious reminiscing to get Miranda's feelings straight for the play.

What are the most common mistakes that occur in productions of your work?
I like to think that mistakes are bound to happen in every production, so I try not to sweat it. You guys shouldn't either.

Try your best and if mistakes happen, it's not the end of the world. It's just another misstep in your ultimate growth as an artist. You can't know how to avoid mistakes until after you've made a few, and all the best artists do.

What inspired you to become a playwright?

For me, becoming a playwright was an essential transition in life. I was initially very inspired by other writers and the glamour of their work, but as I've grown I've realized its value for me personally. Storytelling can be a very cathartic and cleansing experience. Sharing your life and what you've learned is a small part of the job, and I learn something new about myself and how I view my experiences every time I write a play. It would be nice to be inspirational to others as I found other playwrights inspirational when I was younger, but more than anything I'm glad to have found a profession where I can express myself and provide a venue for others to express themselves. It's tremendously important to cultivate a life full of creativity even if your goal isn't to ultimately be an artist. Creativity inspires better thinking and helps you become more empathetic and understanding.

How did you research the subject?

I pulled from my own experiences when I had braces and also used a bit of imagination to create this world. I often think the worst too quickly when I first hear things and in that respect, I am very similar to all of the characters in this play. I assumed when I got braces at 14 that no one was going to want to kiss me. That ended up being a non-issue fortunately, but the inadequacy was a very real feeling. At the beginning of high school, I was very used to the feeling of romantic rejection, so I can relate to the absolute paranoia revolving around adolescent romance. I can very vividly remember a time where I used to speak to my love interests through friends, and I remember just how inefficient that whole process was.

Are any characters modeled after real life or historical figures?

All of the characters in this play are a creation of my imagination, though they certainly exhibit a number of traits and actions that I have experienced in my own life. I had braces like Miranda, and like Tommy, I made an elaborate, wordy necklace with lettered beads. I made mine in the third grade and it said, "I love you, Emily." Like Miranda, she didn't mind how clumsy it was.

Shakespeare gave advice to the players in Hamlet; if you could give advice to your cast what would it be?

You're young, have fun doing this play. Make friends and make really wonderful memories that will last a lifetime. Making art is a collaborative experience, and you won't get anything out of it unless you guys work together. Really listen to each other so you get the timing right. It's true what they say about timing being everything in comedy. Try to think of the play as a piece of music and know when your character is supposed to sing.

About the Author

Keegon Schuett is a playwright, actor, director, and designer who is currently living and working in the Chicago metro area. He was a participant of the Curious New Voices program at Curious Theatre in Denver (CO), and has staged productions of his work at the University of Memphis, where he received his BFA in Theatre. While living in the Memphis area, he appeared in over 20 productions and worked professionally with an educational theatre troupe. He is currently an MFA Playwriting and Screenwriting student at Northwestern University.

RANGER

A short drama by
Nina Ki

CAST OF CHARACTERS

LUIS, a young man in his early teens. The inhabitant of a small town that he desperately wishes to escape from. A strange mixture of a person who has experienced enough of life to have lost some of his innocence, yet still has much to know and live.

TOMMY, Luis's younger brother by a few years, and inhabitant of the same small town, though he does not have the same strong desire to leave. He looks up to and adores his older brother.

(A garden. LUIS, a young boy, carves viciously into the trunk of a tree with a pen knife. His younger brother, TOMMY, enters.)

TOMMY: Luis!

(Startled, Luis turns.)

LUIS: Oh. Tommy. It's you.

TOMMY: *(Breathlessly:)* You ran out so fast. I had to run to keep up, and even then I still —

(Beat. Tommy squints, looking hard at what is in Luis's hand.)

What's that you got?

(Luis shrugs, hiding it behind him.)

LUIS: Don't worry about it.

TOMMY: *(Persistently:)* What is it?

(He goes over to Luis, and tries to look behind him.)

LUIS: I said, don't worry about it.

TOMMY: I want to see —

(Tommy tries to look as Luis holds him at bay, and in the ensuing scuffle, Tommy wrenches it from Luis, falling to the ground.)

LUIS: Tommy, for Chrissake —

(Tommy gasps as he sees what it is.)

TOMMY: Luis, this is Dad's favorite pen knife — the one with the silver handle. *(Pause.)* He's been looking for this for weeks —

LUIS: Shut up, all right? Jesus!

(He grabs the knife from him, and shoves it in his pocket.)

A man can't do nothing 'round here without having some busybody all up in his business —

(Tommy looks hurt, but persists.)

TOMMY: How did you get that? Does he know you have it?

LUIS: None of your business.

TOMMY: I bet he doesn't. If he finds out you have it, he's going to be real mad. Even madder than he was with you before.

LUIS: I said, it's none of your business. And don't you dare tell.

(Beat. Then Tommy shrugs, and stands next to Luis, leaning against the wall like him. A long beat.)

TOMMY: I was worried 'bout you. You ran out so fast—

LUIS: You shouldn't have been.

TOMMY: I know. I mean, I know you can take care of yourself, but— *(Pause.)* I dunno. You looked upset.

(Luis does not answer. Tommy looks again at the knife.)

Can I hold it?

LUIS: Heck no.

TOMMY: Come on, just a little bit?

LUIS: I said, no. You're too young. You could hurt yourself.

TOMMY: You're only fourteen!

LUIS: *(Shrugging:)* I'm older than you.

TOMMY: Only by two years!

LUIS: Well, that still makes me your older brother. And I say no, so—so just shut up for once and listen to me.

(Tommy sulks. Beat.)

TOMMY: Dad was real pissed off at you, huh?

LUIS: Yeah, well, when isn't he?

TOMMY: He didn't hit you too hard, did he?

LUIS: *(Shortly:)* No.

(Long beat.)

TOMMY: I'm sorry, Luis.

LUIS: For what?

TOMMY: I — didn't want him to sell Ranger, either.

LUIS: Well you sure as hell didn't say nothing. *(Pause, bitterly:)* You just stood to the side and watched —

TOMMY: *(Quickly:)* I know. I know. I'm sorry, I just — *(Pause.)* Dad gets so mad, you know how he gets, and he was in such a bad mood —

LUIS: So you were too much of a coward to speak up, then.

TOMMY: No, it's not that, I just — I —

(Luis gives him a piercing look.)

I love Ranger! He's special, and — I know how much you like him — *(Pause.)* I wasn't being a coward.

LUIS: At least I spoke up. Even if Dad hit me —

TOMMY: He hit you because you used curse words. And whined.

LUIS: I did not whine.

TOMMY: Well, it just sounded like —

LUIS: I wasn't whining!!

TOMMY: Okay.

(Luis turns away, shrugging.)

LUIS: Just know that Ranger's gone because of you.

TOMMY: No!! *(Pause, struggling:)* I mean, I was—I just wanted to make sure— *(Pause, then urgently:)* I was going to buy him back!

LUIS: Yeah, right.

TOMMY: No, I was! I have two hundred dollars saved—

(Beat. Luis eyes his brother. Then, snorting and shaking his head:)

LUIS: No, you don't.

TOMMY: I do!

LUIS: Yeah? *(Sarcastically:)* I didn't know you could make money like that doing a paper route—

TOMMY: Don't make fun of me!! *(Pause, then desperately:)* I've been saving it for four years!!

(Luis hesitates, giving Tommy an odd look.)

LUIS: You do not have two hundred dollars.

TOMMY: I saved everything Grandma and Grandpa gave me for every Christmas and birthday. And I put in at least three dollars from what Jem gives me, every week.

(Luis gives his brother another look, deliberating on whether to believe him or not.)

LUIS: Then show me.

TOMMY: It's hidden, at home—

LUIS: Liar. Someone would have found it—

TOMMY: Underneath the couch, under the rug. There's a loose board on the floor, I've been hiding it there. *(Pause.)* I was saving it for a bike. Almost had enough, too, but—when Dad started talking about selling Ranger, I knew I had to buy him. Two hundred is way more than the price of a beagle—

LUIS: *(Shaking his head:)* No, it's not.

TOMMY: What?

LUIS: A beagle is worth three hundred, four hundred easy. Maybe even more.

(He pulls out the knife, and looks at it.)

This knife is worth more than what you got, right now —

TOMMY: Oh. *(Pause.)* Well, maybe if we just talk to whoever bought him —

LUIS: Dad gave him to Joe. The bartender. Dad owes Joe a favor, and Joe was lookin' for a dog to breed his Betsy with, so —

TOMMY: Joe? But isn't he — I mean, didn't he and his family just move to —

LUIS: Up north. Yeah. *(Pause, bitterly:)* It's no use. Ranger's gone.

TOMMY: Oh.

(Long pause. Tommy looks forlorn, almost about to cry. Luis glares at him.)

LUIS: *(Snapping:)* Well don't cry about it!!

TOMMY: *(Turning away:)* I'm not —

(Luis snorts derisively, and turns away. Long beat. Tommy dabs at his eyes with his shirt, and Luis pretends not to notice.)

LUIS: *(Suddenly:)* Let's go get him.

TOMMY: What?

LUIS: Ranger. Let's go get him back.

TOMMY: But isn't he up in —

LUIS: We can get a train ticket.

(They look at each other.)

TOMMY: But — how —

LUIS: We can use your money. And sell the knife. That'll be 'bout five hundred all together, at least, and we can use it to get out there. *(Pause.)* Heck, with that much we can probably even get one of those nice cars you hear about, with a free dinner and velvet seats — won't take much more than a day at most. *(With growing enthusiasm:)* We can get outside this backwards little podunk town, for once.

TOMMY: But— *(Pause.)* But if we use the money on the train, how will we buy Ranger back?

LUIS: We'll — take him. *(Pause.)* We'll find out where they're keeping him, and take him. He's ours, anyway. It wasn't right of Dad to sell him when he's not his —

TOMMY: Well, what about Dad?

LUIS: What about him?

TOMMY: Won't he notice we're gone —

(Luis snorts, and spits.)

LUIS: He could use a little bit of the fear of God in him, anyway. *(Bitterly:)* I hope he sees us gone and chokes on it —

(Tommy swallows, hard. He averts his eyes, saying nothing. Luis claps Tommy on the shoulder.)

Come on, what do you say? I can go over to the pawn shop right now. We can sell the knife, then go down to the train station — Sunday's a good time to leave. Dad'll be out, meeting with that rancher —

TOMMY: *(Slowly:)* I don't know, Luis.

LUIS: *(Snapping:)* Don't be a sissy. It's your being a sissy that got us here, in the first place.

(Tommy looks very hurt. He turns away, and hides his face behind his sleeve.)

What? What now?

(Beat.)

Are you crying again—

TOMMY: *(Yes he is:)* No!!

LUIS: Aww, come on, Tommy.

(Luis goes to touch him on the shoulder, but Tommy jerks away.)

Don't cry— *(Pause.)* I was just—messin' around—

TOMMY: I really did want to stop Dad from selling Ranger.

LUIS: I know that—

TOMMY: And I was saving all that money, for him. Because I love him. And I wanted to make sure we could still have him—

LUIS: All right.

TOMMY: I wasn't trying, to—to be a sissy, I just—if I could take it back now, I would have said something. I wouldn't have let you be the one to get hit and yelled at by Dad, I would have stuck by you and said something too—

(Luis looks at Tommy, looking as if he feels bad. Then he pats Tommy on the back, a little awkwardly.)

LUIS: I—know. *(Pause.)* I know you're not a sissy, Tommy, I'm sorry I called you that. Ranger getting sold was just—I know. I'm sorry.

(Tommy sniffles, and Luis sighs.)

I'm just mad at Dad because he sold Ranger. I'm just sad about it, not mad at you. It wasn't your fault.

(Tommy nods his acceptance of this apology, and the two stand there for a moment. Luis patting Tommy on the back, and Tommy's sniffles subsiding. Long beat.)

TOMMY: We're going to come back though, right, Luis?

LUIS: What?

TOMMY: I know how much you hate this town and sometimes how you hate Dad, but you wouldn't leave, right? 'Cause—you and Dad, and Ranger I guess too, you guys are the only ones I got. *(Pause.)* You're my family, Luis.

LUIS: Well, I—

(He pauses awkwardly, shuffling his feet.)

I know that.

TOMMY: So we can come back, right? We're not going to stay up north? *(Pause.)* I know you like those fancy cars, but maybe we can get maybe just one of those less fancy ones. So we can get another ticket back—

(Long beat. Luis looks at Tommy.)

Luis? *(Pause.)* What do you think?

LUIS: *(Slowly:)* Maybe we shouldn't go.

TOMMY: What? Why?

LUIS: Dad, he'll get worried, and— *(Pause.)* Maybe Ranger's better off with Joe.

TOMMY: Better off? But why? We love Ranger, we'd take good care of him—

LUIS: I know, but—up north, there's a lot more grass, and trees. A lot more green. A dog's got to have a lot of stuff like that to be happy. And there isn't any of that here—

TOMMY: Well, maybe we could get some then. We could plant some trees —

LUIS: No. They'd probably just shrivel up and die here, with how dry it is. *(Pause.)* And with Joe, well — Joe's got a lady dog that he wants to introduce Ranger to. Ranger could have a family. Some pups, and a lot of green — that sounds really nice, doesn't it?

TOMMY: Yeah. It does.

LUIS: So he's probably better off with Joe. He can start his own family —

(Tommy gives Luis a long look.)

And you should really save that money for a bike, anyway. It'll help you with your paper route — *(Pause.)* Dad really would kill me if I sold his knife.

(Suddenly, Tommy hugs Luis.)

(Half-heartedly:) Aww, Tommy —

(He ruffles Tommy's hair, smiling weakly.)

TOMMY: One day we'll take one of those fancy train cars. We'll take it up north, or wherever you want — anywhere in the world.

LUIS: Yeah.

(Light begins to slowly fade. Luis looks out, longingly.)

One day —

(Fade to black. The end.)

The Author Speaks

Are any characters modeled after real life or historical figures?
A little bit. My brother and I have a very strong bond, and I'm pretty sure that growing up, I was a lot like Tommy—forever following and pestering his older brother. In fact, the name "Tommy" comes from a childhood stuffed animal that my brother gave me on my birthday. I also think that there is a little piece of me in Luis—he's caught in a strange place between being a child and growing up, and being a member of your family and part of your environment, and finding your own place in the world. I have definitely experienced that.

What inspired you to write this play?
A while back, when I wrote this play, my friend had sent me an e-mail about this dog that her brother had found, Ranger. Ranger had been in an accident, and he was very hurt—when her brother found him, he was shivering underneath a car, covered in oil, and a lot of his bones were broken. My friend's brother sent everyone he knew an e-mail telling what had happened, asking for funds for a surgery that could help him, and in the e-mail was a video of Ranger running around. I got teary watching the video, and it struck me how much animals and pets could evoke that kind of depth of emotion. Thus, this play was born.

Have you dealt with the same theme in other works that you have written?
I've written another full-length play involving similar themes—living in a small town and the desire to escape, the struggle with obligation to family over self. In fact, I would consider the characters in *Ranger* a younger version of the two brothers I write about in this other play. My relationship with my brother has really come to be one that has defined who I

am, so I think it makes sense that this would come out in a lot of my writing.

What writers have had the most profound effect on your style?

There are so many writers that I enjoy — David Auburn, Diana Son, Anton Chekhov, Sarah Kane, Sarah Ruhl, David Lindsay-Abaire, Tennessee Williams, Martin McDonagh, Jose Rivera, Chay Yew, Henrik Ibsen, Federico Garcia Lorca — just to name a few. I think that everyone I read, playwrights or not, whether I liked their work or not, has an influence on what I write, because it shapes my perspective and my consciousness. I think this also applies to work beyond writing, as well — Helmut Newton is one of my favorite photographers, and he once said that all his photographs were stories without beginnings or endings. This idea definitely applies to writing plays as well. Art always influences other art.

What are the most common mistakes that occur in productions of your work?

Some of my work deals with really serious, dramatic issues, and sometimes the people who work on my play have the tendency to try to convey that really serious emotion by blowing it up and making it REALLY. BIG. EMOTION. Since that work is so serious and dramatic already, sometimes when that really big emotion is there, it makes the work seem more melodramatic. So for some of my work, I think smaller might be better. There's so much that can be conveyed in the small things — a brief smile, the way you say a simple "Goodbye."

What inspired you to become a playwright?

I kind of fell into it by accident. In high school, I fell in love for the first time, with someone who rekindled my interest in writing. We were also in Drama club together. For a while, I even thought I might be interested in becoming an actress, because I really liked the creative expression that happens when you become a character. Then when I was choosing a college to go to, I saw that NYU offered dramatic writing—a combination of the two things I liked the most. Before I went into that program, I had never written a monologue, play, or scene before—and then I really loved it. When I tell this story, it makes me think of falling in love, because it happened twice—with a person, and with playwriting!

Shakespeare gave advice to the players in *Hamlet*; if you could give advice to your cast what would it be?
I think sometimes a lot of people underestimate younger people, and don't take their experiences as seriously as they might the experiences of an adult. The advice I would give would be, don't forget that your voice is important, and let that come out in your acting. So many young people have lived and dealt with so much—don't let anyone tell you differently!

About the Author

Nina Ki graduated from New York University's Tisch School of the Arts with a Bachelor of Fine Arts in Dramatic Writing. Her plays have been read and produced in InspiraTO Theatre's Ten Minute Play Festival, Another Country Productions' SLAMBoston and SLAMBoston Uncensored, in the Kennedy Center American College Theater Festival, in Mixed Phoenix Theater Company's Annual Fall Reading Series, and in the City Theatre of Independence Playwrights Festival. Her poetry has been published in *Relationships and Other Stuff*, as well as the *Getting Bi* poetry anthology. She is the co-founder of Pearl Girls Productions, and through this independent production group is producer and writer of an Asian American webseries. She is also a member of Koreans United for Equality, an alliance of multigenerational straight and LGBTQI Korean Americans committed to promoting sexual and gender equality. When she is not writing, directing, producing, or acting, she advocates for progressive, multicultural education as an elementary school teacher.

CONFESSIONS OF
A PEANUT BUTTER ADDICT

A short comic monologue by
Allan Bates

CAST OF CHARACTERS

SARA, female, a teenager.

SARA: It all started when I was in the second grade. My mother says it was when I was in the first grade. But I know it wasn't. We've had that argument hundreds of times. Or probably really dozens. Dozens at least. Not really arguments. Discussions. She thinks...my mother, that is. She thinks it was when I was in first grade because that's when I met Annabel. I did meet Annabel when she moved next door to us and that was in first grade. But the problem was when I met Emily when she transferred into our school, my school, Maple Avenue Elementary School, when I was in second grade.

Emily had gone to Ben Franklin Elementary and she wasn't very happy there because people teased her. I never knew why because Emily was—still is—a very nice girl. And smart. And she always brought the best sandwiches to school for lunch every day. She... But first, let me tell you about Annabel's sandwiches. Really interesting! They'd have things like olive spread or arugula—I still don't know what arugula is. And Annabel would sit right there next to me and open her sandwich and say, "This is arugula" or whatever. And she'd stick her finger between the leaves of arugula and find maybe some weird cheese that she'd tell me the name of but I couldn't ever remember and then put the sandwich back together and ask me if I'd like a bite... Annabel always started her sandwich with a huge bite. When she took that huge bite and I said, "Yuk," she always had this funny little look on her face like she was almost ready to cry. So after a while, about October I think it was, I started saying, "No thank you, Annabel." Then she'd take that huge bite with a smile on her face. I think that's when I learned to be really polite. Like I am now. I hope you've noticed that.

So you see, Annabel wasn't the problem and it wasn't in first grade. No matter what my mother says.

The problem was when Emily transferred into Maple Avenue Elementary School in second grade. Right from the start Emily became friends with Annabel and me. And we'd all sit together at the same table in the lunch room. And Emily would bring these delicious sandwiches. Peanut butter and jelly! Peanut butter in every sandwich! Sometimes with grape jelly, which was all right, but sometimes with strawberry jam or apricot jam or peach jam. All of them delicious! Believe me, I know they were delicious because Emily used to give me a bite every single day!

Well, she didn't give me a bite at first but after a few days she could see I really wanted to taste her sandwich and that's when she started to say, "Go ahead and try a bite." She saw I wanted to try her sandwich because I'd be sitting there with carrot strips wrapped in wax paper and held together with a rubber band and raisins in the same kind of package. And an apple or a banana and usually some cheese, yellow cheese, and crackers. But always carrot strips and raisins. And sometimes I didn't even open them.

At first I'd take a little nibble of Emily's sandwich and want more. Pretty soon she'd say, "Go ahead, take a big bite." And before long I was taking a huge bite every day and Emily would just smile at me and I'd say, "Thank you." Which is not easy to say when you have peanut butter sticking to your teeth. I could always tell if it was Emily's mother who made the sandwich that day or if Emily made it herself. Because when Emily made the sandwich she always put the jam in there extra thick. And usually it was strawberry when she made it. And those days we'd always have some strawberry jam on our chins and peanut butter on our teeth when we were done. Emily always offered Annabel a bite too, but Annabel always said, "No thank you" and went on with her sandwich. Though sometimes when she put her finger in her sandwich she'd push something really strange looking out of it.

I suppose you think all this isn't why I became a peanut butter addict. But it is.

One day when I came home from school Mother wasn't there. She was just next door, but I didn't know that. And I was hungry. It had to be a day when Emily's mother had made her sandwich and put in something like grapefruit marmalade which would mean I didn't even taste a little bite. I still can't stand grapefruit marmalade. Anyway, I looked in the kitchen cabinets for something to eat. There were cans of soup and boxes of tea and stuff and of course a roll of waxed paper, but I didn't find anything to eat. So I climbed up on the sink and looked into the cabinet up there. And I found peanut butter. Not just one jar of peanut butter, but six jars of peanut butter! Creamy. Crunchy. And extra crunchy. All of them open except one jar of extra crunchy. I climbed down off the sink and got a spoon and ate a whole spoonful out of each jar! Well, each open jar. They were all delicious! Even without strawberry jam.

After a few days of that—me climbing up and eating spoonfuls of peanut butter when, well like when my mother was doing the laundry— she wondered where all her peanut butter had gone. Actually, she knew.

But I should tell you first—one day I was sure Mother was going to catch me. I heard her footsteps coming near. I climbed down from the sink as fast as I could and got away. I was pretty sure she didn't hear me. Didn't hear me or see me after all.

I'll bet you know sort of what happened. The peanut butter jars got emptier and emptier. And, well, as the peanut butter jars got emptier and emptier, I tried to take less and less each day. But it didn't seem to work. It seemed like the harder I tried to take less the more was gone out of each jar. After maybe a week or two, I tried the unopened jar, the extra crunchy jar, and this time I found it was open. I ate a tiny spoonful. I put a bigger spoonful of it in the crunchy jar and smoothed it to look like it belonged in that jar. I turned the lids on the crunchy jar and the extra crunch jar extra tight and hurried to my room.

The next day I didn't even touch that extra crunchy jar. I really didn't.

But the day after that...soon after I came home from school...while I was in my room with the door shut, I heard a sound, like feet shuffling, outside my door. Then nothing. All quiet. Then I heard a gentle knock on my door. Then quiet again. Then I heard Mother say, "Sara." Just, "Sara." Her voice sounded... Well, I knew it was Mother's voice, but I'd never heard her voice like that before. Very quiet. Almost like she'd never called me Sara before.

My own voice seemed to stick in my throat. Then, I said, "Yes." Kind of lower than usual, trying to sound calm.

"Sara, may I come in?" She had never asked me before if she could come in. She had just knocked on the door once, waited a second, and then come in.

She didn't come in.

"Sara?"

"Yes."

Then she opened the door ever so slowly and stood quietly at the doorway.

She was crying. She said, "Sara, I know you've been eating my peanut butter." And I started to cry. Then we both cried together. Just looking at each other and crying. And finally, Mother said, "I've tried to shield you from it." She walked over to me. And we both cried for a long time. Her hugging me and both of us crying. Right in my bedroom. Like I said, for a long time.

Since then... Well, I can't help it. I just can't. Every day I have to eat spoonfuls of peanut butter. Every day. Every single day. Mother says it's all her fault. And sometimes she cries again when she says that. I don't blame her though. I guess it's just in our genes. Our DNA. We're both peanut butter addicts.

But if you...

I'm sorry... I thought I could get all through this without getting all emotional.

But... But if you hear of a PBA group...or a good counselor for this sort of thing... I wish you'd let me know.

   (The end.)

The Author Speaks

What inspired you to write this play?
My eighth-grade granddaughter had just done only moderately well in an oratory contest. When she recited her quite somber speech for me, my response was immediately "This girl is much too gorgeous to be taken seriously." She really is! And very shortly after, I happened to look in her family cupboard and discovered six open jars of peanut butter. Really! The rest became immediate history.

Was the structure of the play influenced by any other work?
I did a PhD dissertation on Mark Twain; I'm quite sure his use of spoken language influenced me. And I'm a great listener. Language has structure.

What writers have had the most profound effect on your style?
Writers with a very strong sense of rhythm. Shakespeare. Lewis Carroll. And writers who are very specific with details. Mark Twain, of course. Katherine Mansfield.

What are the most common mistakes that occur in productions of your work?
Not catching the rhythms. One director of a very successful work of mine began the first rehearsal by saying "All of Allan's plays remind me of various kinds of music." Maybe *Confessions of a Peanut Butter Addict* is like one of those silly songs sung by the campfire on a summer evening.

What inspired you to become a playwright?
Love this question! I was watching my kids on a playground. The rhythms are fantastic! All is so lovely when the swings are going in harmony...but it gets nasty if the bad kid has shortened one rope or chain. Or if the easy fun of building a sand castle is blasted by someone throwing sand. My very first play was produced with a play by Ionesco and another by Pirandello. Wow! I was hooked. Perhaps this is the place to add that I was a wrestler and wrestling coach. While wrestling, one plots out what one hopes to happen in the next

few moves. Great wrestlers have a great sense of balance and rhythm.

Shakespeare gave advice to the players in *Hamlet*; if you could give advice to your cast what would it be?
Just say the words. Talk to your audience as if you were talking to one sympathetic person. Don't try too hard. (I spent years as a member of a Chicago improv theatre group where I learned to pay attention to what is going on from moment to moment.)

About the Author

Allan Bates, the author of three successfully produced full-length children's plays and one yet-to-be produced, has forty years' experience as a playwright. For twenty-five years he directed the Creative Writing program at Northeastern Illinois University. He taught playwriting at Victory Gardens Theatre and was Playwright-in-Residence at Raven Theatre, both leading Chicago theatres. He has authored more than thirty full-length and one-act plays produced throughout Chicago, as well as in New York, Los Angeles and elsewhere. His plays have won Bailiwick Theatre's annual new play award, an Illinois Arts Council $1000 Excellence Award, and acceptance at the University of Michigan Experimental Theatre Festival. Two of his plays have been translated and produced in foreign languages. Recently he has branched out into new directions, including screenwriting and directing a Shakespeare workshop at the Federal Penitentiary in Terre Haute, Indiana. He is a current member of The Dramatists Guild and The Playwrights Center. His website is http://allanbates.com.

HI, WE THOUGHT YOU WERE DEAD

A short dramedy by
Kenyon Brown

CAST OF CHARACTERS

CONNOR, male, any race, age 13. Eighth grader. Smart, wise.

LUKE, male, any race, age 14. Eighth grader. Flakey.

WILLIAM, male, any race, age 14. Eighth grader. Easy going.

ANDREW, male, any race, age 13. Eighth grader. Serious, emotional.

SETTING

Boys' locker room in a middle school gym.

TIME

The present. Morning, during a school day.

SUGGESTED PROPS

Basketball, uniforms, backpacks, cell phones.

PRODUCTION NOTES

This play is intended for middle school and high school students. It might not be appropriate for younger audiences.

(*Locker room. Morning, during a school day. CONNOR and LUKE are changing into warm-up basketball uniforms. Luke is bouncing a basketball. WILLIAM enters. Connor and Luke freeze, stare at William.*)

WILLIAM: What?

CONNOR: Hi…William…

LUKE: You're not dead?

CONNOR: Dude, I never believed it.

LUKE: Me neither.

CONNOR: Yes, you did.

LUKE: Well, I mean I did like for a moment. But then you didn't think he was dead. Then I thought for sure you must be right. No way William is dead. Not with the game tonight. He can't play if he's dead. We can't win if he's dead. So he must be alive.

WILLIAM: I am alive.

LUKE: Obviously.

WILLIAM: What are you talking about?

CONNOR: Dude, we thought you were dead.

LUKE: Yeah.

CONNOR: The text message from your dad.

WILLIAM: My dad? Connor, why would my dad text you?

LUKE: I got a text, too. He texted everyone.

CONNOR: He said he was texting everyone in your contact list about your accident.

WILLIAM: Accident?

CONNOR: You were walking across the street when a car hit you…

LUKE: And didn't stop. A hit and ruin.

CONNOR: Hit and run.

LUKE: Yeah, a hit and run. Totally cold.

WILLIAM: My dad just dropped me off. I was at the dentist.

LUKE: Oh, I hate the dentist.

CONNOR: Your dad said you died in the ambulance.

LUKE: I'm supposed to get a wisdom tooth removed.

CONNOR: Luke, focus. It's on Facebook, too.

LUKE: And everyone's tweeting about it.

CONNOR: Haven't you read your wall? Or seen the "Likes" on Instagram?

(Luke takes phone out of pocket. Boys gather around cell phone.)

WILLIAM: "…totally heinous act…beyond comprehension…" My dad doesn't say stuff like that. And now people think I'm dead?

LUKE: This is the most badass thing that's ever happened to us.

WILLIAM: To us?

LUKE: Well, I mean we're like bros, right?

CONNOR: William, you have to text people you're not dead.

LUKE: Yeah, William, you shouldn't pretend you're dead. It's not like pretending you're sick and you stay home playing Halo 3.

WILLIAM: Luke, I'm not pretending I'm dead.

LUKE: Well, everybody thinks you're dead.

CONNOR: People are like hysterical. They've been crying. Even teachers. Even Coach.

LUKE: Yeah, Coach led us in saying a prayer for you and your family.

WILLIAM: This is so whack.

LUKE: I wish people would say a prayer for me.

CONNOR: Dude, you need all the prayers you can get. Will you focus on William, please? How could your dad text us from your phone?

WILLIAM: My phone?

LUKE: It was definitely from your phone.

CONNOR: Did your dad take your phone away from you?

LUKE: I hate it when my parents take my phone privileges away.

CONNOR: Luke...

LUKE: I know. Focus.

WILLIAM: I misplaced it... I've been searching everywhere...

LUKE: You lost your phone?

WILLIAM: Maybe. I don't know.

CONNOR: When?

WILLIAM: Friday, I think. I thought it was in my back pocket.

LUKE: Did it fall into the toilet?

CONNOR: How could it fall into the toilet when his dad texted us with William's phone?

LUKE: Oh, right.

WILLIAM: My dad didn't text anyone.

LUKE: Never take a dump and text at the same time. What?

CONNOR: Did you check your backpack?

WILLIAM: Yes, I checked it.

CONNOR: It's a 9-1-1, dude.

LUKE: Definitely a 9-1-1.

CONNOR: Someone knows your phone password.

WILLIAM: I don't password my phone.

CONNOR: Whoa. Not good.

LUKE: Definitely not good.

CONNOR: You have to tell your parents.

WILLIAM: I am sooo dead…

LUKE: That's funny. I mean since you're supposed to be dead but you're really not.

CONNOR: You have to cancel your phone.

WILLIAM: I know…

LUKE: I hate telling my parents every time I lose my phone.

CONNOR: How many times have you lost your phone?

LUKE: A few…

WILLIAM: I can't believe this is happening.

LUKE: How else could somebody be texting everyone from your phone?

WILLIAM: And change my Facebook password. My password doesn't work anymore.

CONNOR: You can't get into Facebook?

LUKE: This is so not good.

CONNOR: Ya think?

(ANDREW enters. He sees William, freezes.)

WILLIAM: What'll people say when they find out?

LUKE: People really love you now that you're dead.

WILLIAM: But I'm not dead.

LUKE: Then people will love you even more when they find out you're alive.

(Andrew rushes over to William, hugs him.)

WILLIAM: I'm not dead, Andrew.

LUKE: See? He's loved.

CONNOR: Dude, get emotional, why don't you?

WILLIAM: You can let go of me now, Andrew.

(Andrew lets go of William.)

ANDREW: I don't understand…

CONNOR: Like none of us do.

LUKE: William, you can go to the office. Tell them to make an announcement you're not dead.

CONNOR: Just like that?

LUKE: It's faster than texting.

ANDREW: How could…?

WILLIAM: Someone's ripped off my phone and texting with it.

ANDREW: There are all these flowers and pictures of you by your locker.

WILLIAM: Really?

LUKE: I lit a candle for you.

CONNOR: Dude, you lit a candle?

LUKE: I like candles.

ANDREW: People are like shocked.

WILLIAM: I have to go to my locker and get my books.

ANDREW: If you go to your locker, you'll shock people even more...

LUKE: You mean we're the only ones who know you're not dead?

WILLIAM: I guess. When my dad dropped me off, I walked straight to the gym.

CONNOR: You should find Coach and tell him before practice starts.

LUKE: But just don't walk out of the locker room and say, "Surprise! I'm not dead!" Say it but like positively. "I'm alive! I'm alive!"

CONNOR: Are you for real?

WILLIAM: But it's not my fault.

LUKE: *(To Andrew:)* Wait. What are you doing here?

CONNOR: Yeah, this is just for the starters. We have permission from our teachers to be here.

LUKE: Yeah, you don't have permission.

ANDREW: Coach said I should come.

LUKE: But you're second string. You don't practice with us.

ANDREW: I'm starting in the game tonight.

WILLIAM: You're replacing me?

LUKE: That's cold when you're not really dead.

ANDREW: Coach is giving me a chance.

CONNOR: You can't center.

LUKE: Yeah, you're too short.

ANDREW: No, I'm not. Anyway, it's not all about height.

CONNOR: Dude, it's about having the hands.

LUKE: And you definitely don't got the hands.

ANDREW: I do too.

CONNOR: You're more a small forward.

LUKE: Definitely a small forward.

ANDREW: I'm a good center.

LUKE: For second string maybe.

CONNOR: You're not as good as William.

WILLIAM: Talk about me like I'm not here, why don't you?

CONNOR: It is so wrong you're starting, Andrew.

LUKE: So wrong.

WILLIAM: I can't believe the game's still on.

LUKE: It's not like we want to play without you. Coach said you'd want us to continue.

CONNOR: Dude, the game has to go on.

LUKE: Yeah, the game has to go on.

CONNOR: It's the best way to honor your memory.

LUKE: You don't want us to be sad, do you?

CONNOR: We're dedicating the rest of the season to you.

WILLIAM: Hel-lo-oo, I'm not dead!

LUKE: William's right. He's not dead.

(*Connor starts texting on phone.*)

ANDREW: I think I should still suit up. Coach told me to.

CONNOR: I'll text Coach to come to the locker room.

ANDREW: But he'll see William isn't dead.

CONNOR: Du-uh.

ANDREW: But I won't start.

WILLIAM: Connor, don't send the text. I'll go talk to Coach.

LUKE: When William walks into his office, Coach'll think it's like a miracle.

CONNOR: Only if William was really dead, dufus.

LUKE: Then actually William would be like a zombie.

ANDREW: Dead, then not dead.

LUKE: The undead, exactly.

ANDREW: I don't know how William's going to explain this.

WILLIAM: I am standing here, you know.

ANDREW: People will be really upset. Maybe you shouldn't play.

WILLIAM: It's not my fault people think I died.

LUKE: Then people will cheer when you run out on court.

ANDREW: Or they'll boo.

WILLIAM: Why would they boo me?

ANDREW: You know, like they'll think it's a hoax.

CONNOR: He's right, William. Dude, think about it. People will say you punk'd them.

WILLIAM: I'm the one who's been punk'd.

CONNOR: They don't know that.

LUKE: You'll lose all your cool points.

WILLIAM: Someone's playing a joke on me.

CONNOR: This could be a major backfire. Coach could bench you for the rest of the season.

LUKE: Or kick you off the team.

CONNOR: At least until he finds out the truth.

(William slams locker door.)

WILLIAM: What can I do?

ANDREW: Stay dead until after the game tonight.

LUKE: Whoa, that's harsh.

ANDREW: It'll give you time to think of what you're going to say.

WILLIAM: What about me playing in the game?

ANDREW: I'll take your place like Coach wants me to.

WILLIAM: That means you'll start as center.

ANDREW: I can do it. I'll play the best I've ever played. William, you won't be sorry.

WILLIAM: How can this be happening when I didn't do anything wrong?

ANDREW: I have to play. It's the only way Coach will see I can do it.

CONNOR: With William, we have a shot at being in the finals.

ANDREW: Are you saying we don't with me playing?

LUKE: You haven't played much all season.

ANDREW: Only because Coach hasn't put me in.

LUKE: For a reason.

WILLIAM: Okay, okay — this is not helping.

ANDREW: I'm just as good as William.

LUKE: I don't think so.

ANDREW: I deserve to play. Why are you all against me?

CONNOR: Andrew, chill.

WILLIAM: Everyone chill.

LUKE: This is the most jank of anything bad that's ever happened.

CONNOR: The person who did this is really cold.

LUKE: Bogus.

ANDREW: Beyond comprehension.

CONNOR: Messed up.

WILLIAM: Definitely twisted.

LUKE: Not funny.

ANDREW: A totally heinous act.

WILLIAM: So gnarly.

LUKE: You sound like the text.

WILLIAM: What?

LUKE: Andrew, I mean.

ANDREW: What are you saying?

LUKE: That's what William's dad texted.

ANDREW: No…

CONNOR: Yeah.

WILLIAM: How many times do I have to say my dad didn't text anything!

LUKE: I mean what the person who was pretending to be your dad texted. If he was your dad. But of course he wasn't. So he couldn't have texted you're dead. Your dad, I mean.

CONNOR: Luke's right.

LUKE: I am?

CONNOR: That was what the person texted.

WILLIAM: The same words.

ANDREW: Say what?

WILLIAM: "Beyond comprehension...totally heinous act." Those are definitely not my dad's words.

ANDREW: I was just repeating the text I read.

LUKE: But like word for word verbal?

CONNOR: Verbatim.

LUKE: Yeah, verbatim?

WILLIAM: Show us the text you got.

ANDREW: I left my phone at home.

CONNOR: How'd you read the text then?

ANDREW: Somebody showed me their phone.

WILLIAM: I don't believe you.

ANDREW: I don't care what you believe. I have to suit up.

WILLIAM: There's no need.

ANDREW: Coach said I'm starting tonight.

WILLIAM: No, you're not. I'm here. Nothing changes.

ANDREW: William, I don't know how this happened, but it happened.

WILLIAM: Because of you, I bet!

ANDREW: People are totally upset you're dead.

WILLIAM: You probably ripped off my phone. Did you steal it out of my gym locker?

ANDREW: You're just going to upset people more if you walk out on court like nothing happened.

WILLIAM: You sent the text, Andrew! Didn't you!

ANDREW: Stop saying that!

WILLIAM: Why, Andrew? What did I ever do to you?

LUKE: It was you who sent the text.

ANDREW: I didn't. I swear…

CONNOR: Poser.

LUKE: Yeah, poser.

WILLIAM: You just said the same words in the text.

ANDREW: How many times do I have to say it wasn't me?

CONNOR: Blah blah blah.

LUKE: Wah wah wah.

ANDREW: We have to focus on the game tonight.

WILLIAM: Why is playing so important to you?

ANDREW: If we win, it'll clinch us a spot in the finals.

WILLIAM: You texted everyone I was dead so you can play?

ANDREW: No…

CONNOR: Dude, that is totally heinous.

LUKE: And like beyond comprehension.

WILLIAM: You're so pathetic.

ANDREW: William, with you showing up suddenly, it won't be about the game anymore. You'll make it about you.

WILLIAM: No, Andrew, you've made this all about you.

CONNOR: Yeah.

LUKE: Yeah.

(William, Connor, and Luke surround Andrew.)

(Lights fade. End of play.)

The Author Speaks

What inspired you to write this play?

Social media hoaxes and cyberbullying is getting rampant, especially among young people. It's hurtful and often destructive. All of us need to learn to use social media websites responsibly, because we're posting a lot of details about our personal and professional lives on the web. It's amazing how many people think posting details about themselves on the web remain "private." The fact is we're exposing details about ourselves in public for anyone to read. If you've ever been the victim of a social media hoax or the target of cyberbullying, you know how upsetting it is because it's very difficult—and practically impossible--to do anything about it. However, if you discover the perpetrator, you need to confront the person, and stop it.

Have you dealt with the same theme in other works that you have written?

I have written about using Twitter as a tool that a girl and her mother use to communicate with each other. However, this is the first time I've written about a social media hoax that goes very wrong. I wanted to explore how an act of cyberbullying can be dangerous and destructive.

What do you hope to achieve with this work?

I hope young people will understand they need to use social media responsibly. It's a wonderful tool for sharing details about our lives with other people. At the same time, some misguided people have started using social media as a weapon. They use it in a destructive way because they think they can remain anonymous and not get caught. However, all of us need to be vigilant, and confront these people when we find out who they are. I don't want young people to be complacent or apathetic, and think they're powerless to stop social media hoaxes and cyberbullying. They can; sometimes all it takes is standing up to such people and outing them.

Are any characters modeled after real life or historical figures?
My two nieces and their friends often serve as models for characters in my plays. Since social media is so integrated in their lives, the girls' parents are always talking to them about appropriate online behavior and etiquette. Now that their younger brother has a smartphone and is starting to use social media websites, the girls are giving him tips about using the sites. They're also trying to impart their knowledge and wisdom, i.e. what to do and what not to do online. They've told him horror stories about how some of their friends have gotten into trouble online. It's interesting to hear them discuss situations in which they're aware that cyberbullying of people they know is going on, but they're not speaking up. I realize they feel they have to tread carefully. However, I tell them confronting people who are bullying other people online is the right thing to do.

Shakespeare gave advice to the players in Hamlet; if you could give advice to your cast what would it be?
Have fun! It's a play—so play! Even with a serious play, you can enjoy the experience. I know I expect a lot of younger actors in my plays. I want you to bring your experiences, feelings, and points of views to the characters you play. I want you to find your own truths in the roles you take on. I want you to be authentic and show vulnerability. I want you to be honest. The audience will respond positively to you when you're honest. Keep it real—even when you're acting.

About the Author

See **Kenyon Brown**'s bio after *My Big Adele Moment* on page 47.

THE UnderGroundHog RAILROAD

A short dramedy by
Jeri Weiss

CAST OF CHARACTERS

JAYDEN, male; environmentally conscious middle school student.

BREE, female; materialistic middle school student.

SETTING

A neighborhood outdoors.

NOTES

The "iPhone" can be changed to the newest, most popular cell phone at the time of production. A stuffed animal may be used as the groundhog, or the actors can pantomime holding one.

(JAYDEN sits on a bench. He has something hidden in his jacket.)

JAYDEN: I'm sorry, Harry. I wish I could keep you.

(BREE enters and sees Jayden talking into his jacket.)

BREE: What are you doing?

(Startled, Jayden closes his jacket.)

Who are you talking to?

JAYDEN: Nobody.

BREE: *(Looking at his jacket:)* What do you have in there?

JAYDEN: Nothing.

BREE: Then why is your jacket moving?

(Jayden pulls a baby groundhog from his jacket.)

Oh my gosh. What is that?

JAYDEN: It's a *Marmota monax.* A member of the *Sciuridae* family.

BREE: In English.

JAYDEN: It's a baby groundhog.

(Bree sits next to Jayden.)

BREE: It's so cute. Where did you get it?

JAYDEN: I found him. I named him Harry.

BREE: Hi, Harry. Aww. I want one.

JAYDEN: You can't have one.

BREE: Why not?

JAYDEN: They're illegal in our state.

BREE: How can an animal be illegal?

JAYDEN: It's an invasive species.

BREE: What does that mean?

JAYDEN: They're not native to the area.

BREE: So what? This is America, right? It's a free country.

JAYDEN: You're missing the point. Non-native animals are a threat to our ecosystem.

BREE: How could this sweet little thing be a threat to anyone?

JAYDEN: By eating plants that our own native species need to survive.

BREE: Well, it sounds like a stupid law to me.

JAYDEN: Well, it's not.

BREE: Are your parents letting you keep him?

JAYDEN: Yeah, right. They won't even let me have a goldfish. They're calling Animal Control.

BREE: Animal Control. They can't do that. They'll kill him, won't they? Let's just take him back where you found him and let him go.

JAYDEN: Weren't you listening to what I just said? They endanger the ecosystem.

BREE: You and your ecosystem.

JAYDEN: *Our* ecosystem.

BREE: Well, you can't just let them take him.

JAYDEN: What else am I supposed to do with him? Would your parents let you keep him?

BREE: My mom might, but my dad threatened to leave if we brought home one more pet.

JAYDEN: Is your dad as cute as this little guy?

BREE: No, but this little guy is not gonna buy me a new iPhone.

JAYDEN: Materialist.

(Bree tries to think of a comparable insult, but the best she can come up with is:)

BREE: Environmentalist.

(Jayden laughs.)

Can I hold him?

(Jayden pulls Harry away from her.)

JAYDEN: I think he's hungry. I need to feed him.

BREE: I'm not going to let him go. You can feed him in a minute.

JAYDEN: Alright.

(Bree takes Harry.)

BREE: Hi little guy— *(Holding him in front of her:)* Uh, I hate to break it to you, but I think Harry is a Harriet.

JAYDEN: Oh. I didn't notice.

BREE: You wouldn't.

JAYDEN: What's that supposed to mean?

BREE: Nothing. *(To the groundhog:)* You're a pretty little girl, aren't you, Harriet? Look at your big belly. You're a tubby little thing. You're a little Harriet Tubman.

JAYDEN: Harriet Tubman. That's funny. *(Beat.)* No, that's not funny; that's brilliant.

BREE: Huh?

JAYDEN: Harriet Tubman. You know who she is, don't you?

BREE: Didn't she have something to do with slavery?

JAYDEN: Uh, yeah? Ever heard of the Underground Railroad?

BREE: That's how she got the slaves free, right? She built a railroad.

JAYDEN: It wasn't an actual railroad. It was a network of people who helped move the slaves from town to town until they reached a free state.

BREE: Okay, well, thanks for the history lesson.

JAYDEN: Don't you see? That's how we're going to set Harriet free. We're going to set up an underground railroad to a free state.

BREE: But...she's not African American.

(Jayden just looks at her.)

JAYDEN: Really? *(Beat.)* I'm talking about taking her someplace where groundhogs aren't illegal. Like...Punxsutawney.

BREE: Punx-a-what-ey?

JAYDEN: It's a town in Pennsylvania.

BREE: That would take a really long tunnel.

JAYDEN: The underground railroad wasn't actually underground, you know.

BREE: Well, that's dumb. Why did they call it that?

JAYDEN: Because it was done in secret.

BREE: Oh, like undercover.

JAYDEN: Right.

BREE: So how do we do it?

JAYDEN: I have a friend who lives in Winchester. I can make it there on my bike in about three hours. I take Harriet with me and drop her off with Jess. Then Jess rides his bike to someone who lives a few hours north from him, and it continues like that.

BREE: So it would be like an Under-ground-hog Railroad?

(Jayden smiles at her.)

JAYDEN: Yeah. We just need someone at the other end who can release her in a safe place.

BREE: My cousin lives in Maryland. She could probably get Harriet over the border.

JAYDEN: So if we can find enough people from here to your cousin's house, we can transport her to freedom.

BREE: How do we do that?

JAYDEN: We need to call everyone we know between here and Maryland.

(They get out their phones. Bree's is woefully outdated.)

What kind of phone is that?

BREE: I know, right? That's why I need the new iPhone.

JAYDEN: Does it even text?

BREE: Yes, it texts.

(They both move their thumbs like crazy as they text. Then they wait, staring at their phones.)

JAYDEN: Come on, Jess. Be home.

BREE: This phone is so slow.

(After another beat, they both receive texts.)

JAYDEN: Jess is in.

BREE: My cousin says she'll release Harriet for us.

JAYDEN: He has a friend farther north he can take her to.

BREE: She's texting her friend who lives a few hours south of her. *(Beat.)* This is really happening, isn't it?

JAYDEN: Thanks to you it is.

BREE: It was your idea.

JAYDEN: But I wouldn't have thought of it if you hadn't given Harriet her name.

BREE: Thanks to us, then.

JAYDEN: Us. Yes.

> *(Their eyes meet for an awkward beat.)*

Uh, well, I better leave now before my parents get home.

BREE: I wish I could go with you.

JAYDEN: You do?

BREE: You know, to help.

JAYDEN: Oh.

BREE: Text me when you get back. You know, so I'll know she's safe.

JAYDEN: Okay. Maybe we should meet back here this afternoon. You know, to track her progress.

BREE: I'd like that.

JAYDEN: Me too.

> *(Another awkward silence.)*

Well... I better...

BREE: Yeah...

JAYDEN: So I'll see you...

BREE: Okay...

> *(As Jayden exits, Bree calls out to Harriet.)*

Bye, Harriet! Have a safe trip! Enjoy your new ecosystem!

(End of play.)

The Author Speaks

What inspired you to write this play?

I used to volunteer with a wildlife rescue organization. I took care of orphaned baby squirrels, feeding them every few hours with a tiny syringe, until they were healthy enough to be released into the wild. Occasionally, I would take care of injured tortoises. They had traveled a long way from home and they had wounds on their feet. I would have to pull their feet out from the shell to put ointment on them, but I had to be quick because they have long necks and they will bite your fingers! I found out that these tortoises were not native species and we were not allowed to release them in the wild. Fortunately, we were able to find good homes for the tortoises, but the experience made me wonder how a person might go about getting an orphaned animal safely to its native environment.

Have you dealt with the same theme in other works that you have written?

I love animals, so my plays often have characters that go to extremes to help them. For example, in my play *Purge*, two boys break into a science lab to rescue frogs from being used in experiments. While they are punished for their actions, they are successful in eliminating meat from their cafeteria menu (yes, I am a vegetarian!). I also like to incorporate topics that students are learning about, such as history or literature, into my plays to show how they are still relevant in our lives today. My play *Before You Speak*, for example, links the historic Salem witch trials with a modern story about bullying.

What do you hope to achieve with this work?

I hope the actors and the audience are inspired to help animals in need. It would be wonderful to have more people involved in wildlife rescue, especially since it is often our actions that put these animals in peril. Every time we clear the wilderness to build houses or shopping malls, the animals native to that plot of land are displaced. Wild animals are also often injured by cars or other man-made devices.

What were the biggest challenges involved in the writing of this play?

I was a bit nervous that someone might find it offensive that I used the story of the Underground Railroad in this way. I wanted to make sure that it did not sound as if I were trivializing the great achievements of Harriet Tubman and the other freedom fighters. I hope it inspires the audience to learn more about this amazing woman.

How did you research the subject?

Since I live in California and we don't have groundhogs here, I had to conduct research to find out in what areas of the United States they thrive. I was sad to learn that they are considered "pests" in most states, so much of the information I found was about how to get rid of them!

I chose Pennsylvania as the "free state" destination of the groundhog in my play because of the most famous groundhog of all time: Punxsutawney Phil. Each year, on Groundhog Day, there is a big ceremony in the small Pennsylvania town of Punxsutawney to celebrate the groundhog's "ability" to predict a long winter or an early spring. According to legend, Phil pops up from hibernation on February 2nd. If he does not see his shadow and goes back to his hole, this means there will be six more weeks of winter-like weather. If, however, Phil *does* see his shadow, this means that spring-like weather is coming early.

This event is the only pro-groundhog example I found in my research, so I figured if there were a safe place for the groundhog to live in my story, it would be near this location.

It was also a good choice because Pennsylvania was one of the free states that welcomed fugitive slaves.

Are any characters modeled after real life or historical figures?

Yes. Harriet Tubman and the Underground Railroad are an important part of United States history. Harriet Tubman, an African-American abolitionist, risked her life to help transport slaves to freedom before and during the Civil War. After escaping from slavery herself, she returned to slave territory to help her family members escape. But she did not stop there; she continued to make trips to save others and reportedly led 300 slaves to freedom. There are many museums and monuments in her honor.

The Underground Railroad, as my character explains in the play, was not actually a railroad. In fact, there were many different routes to freedom and many different modes of transportation. It was not as easy as taking a train ride: while some slaves were carried by wagon, many others had to walk, and they were in constant danger of being captured. They stopped at "safe houses" along the way for food and shelter, and they fooled the slaveholders by speaking in code, sometimes even hiding their directions in songs. It was an amazing achievement for everyone involved.

About the Author

Jeri Weiss is a playwright based in Northern California. She received her BA in liberal studies at Mills College, and she will be graduating from Hollins University soon with an MFA in playwriting. Although Jeri writes plays for both adult and youth audiences, she especially enjoys working with and writing for young actors. From rocking babies at a crisis nursery to leading a Girl Scout troop to working in a high school, Jeri has always found inspiration from the young people she encounters. Her plays have been produced throughout the United States and Canada and several have been published, including **A Number of Secrets** and **The UnderGroundHog Railroad** by YouthPLAYS, **Before You Speak** by Freshwater Press, and **Lemonade** by Applause Books in the collection *One-on-One: Playing with a Purpose*. Jeri is a member of the Dramatists Guild and the Playwrights Lab at Hollins University.

FAMILY MEETING

A short comedy by
Don Zolidis

CAST OF CHARACTERS

MOM

DAD

KAITLYN, a teenager.

SVEN, a foreign exchange student, does not actually have to be a teenager.

(In a living room, DAD and MOM are preparing.)

DAD: You ready for this?

MOM: I don't know if I can do this, Bob.

DAD: You can. You can. Remember — we love her.

MOM: We do.

(They grip hands.)

DAD: Sweetheart, could you come in here for a bit? Your mother and I would like to talk to you!

(No response.)

It's important!

KAITLYN: *(Off:)* I'm kinda busy!

MOM: We need to talk to you! It's very important!

(KAITLYN enters, confused.)

KAITLYN: Can we do this quick because — ?

(Mom leaps to her feet and gets between Kaitlyn and her room.)

MOM: Aha!

KAITLYN: What?

DAD: We've got you!

KAITLYN: What? What are you talking about?

DAD: Family Meeting!

KAITLYN: *(Baffled:)* You could've just said that —

DAD: No, no, no. You're not escaping this time. This time we're having a meeting.

MOM: We're having a big meeting. Sit.

(Kaitlyn sits reluctantly.)

KAITLYN: I still don't know what's going on.

DAD: Honey, would you like to tell her?

MOM: I thought you were going to tell her.

DAD: We talked about this. It sounds better coming from you.

MOM: You need to be the voice of authority, Bob.

KAITLYN: What is it?!

DAD: Okay, fine. *(Slight pause.)* Your mother is going to begin.

MOM: There seems to be some tension in the house. We've all been feeling it.

KAITLYN: That's your fault, not mine.

MOM: Can I finish please? I have a list here of things that have bothered me lately about you and your behavior.

> *(She looks at a long list.)*

But you know what? I'm going to skip the minor things and get right to the major problem.

KAITLYN: Major problem?

MOM: It's...

> *(She can't bring herself to say it. She looks to Dad.)*

DAD: You can say it honey. Be strong.

> *(He holds Mom's hand in solidarity.)*

MOM: You're my rock.

DAD: And you're my rock.

KAITLYN: Can we get to it?!

MOM: It's...it's your basketball skills.

KAITLYN: What?

DAD: Let your mother speak. Tell her what we've been thinking about.

MOM: Well...I think we all would prefer someone in this family who can dunk.

KAITLYN: I'm five three.*

(*Or whatever height she happens to be.)

DAD: Spud Webb could dunk. Spud Webb was like four feet tall.

KAITLYN: He was a guy.

MOM: I don't like the way you use your gender as an excuse. A girl can do anything a boy can do.

DAD: When you were young you could dunk. We had that little basketball hoop and you were dunking all the time —

KAITLYN: That was like two feet tall!

DAD: All these excuses from you! Listen to yourself. Don't you even respect who you are? We have high standards for you! And one of them is that we want to see some high-flying jams. Would it kill you to do some windmill 360 thunder dunks on a regulation hoop?!

KAITLYN: I'm a girl!

MOM: Listen young lady, I never want to hear you hiding behind your gender again, you hear me?! Your father's heart is breaking because of your lack of a gravity-defying aerial assault. Look at him. Look at him! He is a sick man because of this! You're killing him!

KAITLYN: I'm not killing him, I just can't dunk!

MOM: I don't think I ever taught you the word "can't." I don't understand how this word got into your vocabulary.

DAD: Ninety percent inspiration. Ten percent perspiration. You think LeBron could dunk if he didn't believe he could dunk?

KAITLYN: Yes. Have you seen him?

DAD: Honey—if you believe in yourself...you can do anything.

MOM: We have tried and tried and tried with you. We've tried reasoning with you, we've tried punishing you, we've tried inspiring you—nothing seems to work.

DAD: So...since this is obviously not working out. We're replacing you.

KAITLYN: What?

MOM: I'm sorry, sweetheart. I wish that I could say love was enough, but after a certain amount of time we need to see results.

KAITLYN: You can't replace me!

DAD: Honey...there's someone we'd like you to meet.

(SVEN enters. Sven doesn't have to be extremely tall, but it would help.)

This is Sven. He's our foreign exchange student.

KAITLYN: What?

SVEN: Ya. Hello.

MOM: He's amazing.

SVEN: Thank you.

KAITLYN: He's a foreign exchange student?

DAD: We just felt like our family worked better with Sven in it. He's...I mean look at him.

MOM: He's really the kind of physical specimen we're looking for in this family.

DAD: It's not all about physical attributes, though—I think your mother and I both felt like his intangibles were off the charts.

MOM: Oh yeah.

SVEN: Ya. I have great intangibles.

KAITLYN: His intangibles?

MOM: Honey—I love you, I really do, and I've made a big commitment to you, but you just don't believe in yourself.

KAITLYN: This is ridiculous! You can't trade me for a foreign exchange student!

DAD: We just felt that he gives our family a lot more presence in the low post.

MOM: Plus, no one has screwed him up mentally like you've obviously been.

KAITLYN: You can't dunk.

DAD: Don't you say that!

MOM: I can't dunk? I can't dunk? I dunked when I was seven months pregnant with you!

DAD: She did! I didn't see it but she told me about it afterwards and this is a marriage built on trust.

MOM: Thank you, Bob.

DAD: No thank you. For being inspirational.

MOM: I'm not inspirational. I'm just one woman.

KAITLYN: I can't do it. I'm never going to be able to do it.

MOM: If only your grandmother could hear you now.

KAITLYN: Grandma couldn't dunk either!

MOM: Grandma couldn't dunk because she wasn't allowed to dunk! Do you know how many women have sacrificed to give you the opportunities you have today? What we went through? The harassment we suffered? And to have you, little miss everything, come along and throw away the opportunity to shatter an opponent's will to fight with a backboard-shattering jam is disgusting!

DAD: I'm disgusted!

SVEN: Ya. Me too.

KAITLYN: What's—what's going to happen to me?

DAD: We're sending you to the farm.

KAITLYN: The same farm where you sent Rufus and he never came back?!

MOM: Honey, you'll like the farm. They have low standards there.

KAITLYN: I'm not going.

DAD: It'll be better for you. You can be amongst your own kind. The earthbound.

KAITLYN: I don't care. I'm not going near any farm. You know why? Because I traded you for new parents!

DAD: What?

MOM: You can't do that!

KAITLYN: Yes I can! I talked to my own therapist and she told me that the reason I couldn't dunk was because I wasn't receiving the right kind of motivation. And where did that come from? From you! If you were any kind of inspirational parents, I would've been dunking years ago. This is all your fault.

MOM: Our therapist said the opposite!

KAITLYN: Too bad! My new parents are going to be arriving any minute now!

DAD: I'd like to see these people.

KAITLYN: And these are parents who are going to get results! They're Canadian!

DAD: That's preposterous!

MOM: Canadian?!

DAD: It's too cold in Canada for anyone to have kids!

KAITYLN: Not true!

SVEN: Sven likes Canadians.

KAITLYN: That's okay, Sven. You can stay.

SVEN: Yay for Sven.

MOM: You can't keep Sven and trade us!

KAITLYN: Watch me! My new Canadian parents are going to be so much more awesome than you ever were. They're going provide consistent boundaries!

DAD: What!

SVEN: Sven likes consistent boundaries.

KAITLYN: And they're going to give me room to self-actualize and allow me to discover my own true self! While simultaneously inspiring me to elevate over any defender and send them home crying with a series of acrobatic slams so devastating they'll never want to play again.

MOM: I...I don't know what to say.

DAD: You'd trade us? After everything we've done for you? Your mother dunked while she was seven months pregnant with you.

KAITLYN: Hey. Guys. Guys. I feel for you. And that's why I've written you a really nice letter of recommendation.

(She takes out a recommendation letter.)

"Children with minor talents may find Bob and Carol acceptable. For those children with the talent to reach the truly dizzying levels of ability, however, their inability to make effective speeches and sacrifice their personal lives will be a drawback." I did have to be honest. Don't worry. You'll catch on somewhere else. Maybe there are some ducks who've lost a mother, or a kindergarten who needs a room parent.

MOM: But these new parents...they won't love you I like do.

KAITLYN: Mom, or should I call you former Mom, these people have already started a college plan for me.

DAD: I feel sick. My heart.

MOM: Wait! Honey—we can change. Right, Bob? We'll change.

DAD: We'll change all over the place!

MOM: We'll never expect anything from you again!

DAD: Or wait—no we'll expect more from you than we ever did before!

MOM: You won't even have to play basketball!

DAD: I'll get some performance enhancing drugs for you!

KAITLYN: It's not either of those things! I just want you to accept the fact that I can't dunk, and I never will.

DAD: No daughter of mine can't dunk.

KAITLYN: Dad?

DAD: Okay. I'll just have to accept the fact that my dreams for you are dead.

MOM: It's for the best.

KAITLYN: I still have a deadly accurate long range shot.

DAD: Well...I guess that's something.

MOM: So you'll call off the Canadian parents?

KAITLYN: They've already been apprehended by the good folks at INS, just like all Canadians.

MOM: Thank goodness.

KAITLYN: So can I go back to studying?

DAD: Sure.

KAITLYN: All right.

(Kaitlyn exits. After a moment:)

SVEN: Soo…what is to become of Sven?

DAD: Don't worry. We're keeping you. If there's one thing I've learned about parenting, it's when to call somebody's bluff. She made her first mistake when she mentioned Canada, which, as everyone knows, is a made-up fantasy land invented to keep people from falling off the top of the world. We're still trading her to the farm.

MOM: Bob…after all these years, you still amaze me.

DAD: Thanks, honey. All right! New family photo!

(Sven leans in and Dad takes out a phone.)

Say cheese!

(He takes a selfie. Blackout. End of play.)

The Author Speaks

What inspired you to write this play?

This is satire, obviously. And a good satire requires a good target. It seems to me that parents often feel judged by the accomplishments and abilities of their children, so I wanted to take a stab at that in this play, as well as the idea that "if you work hard and you believe in yourself, you can accomplish anything." That's the message that our culture seems to be perpetuating, which isn't a terrible message in and of itself, but when you think about it, it's incredibly false. Well, no, that's not true. You can't accomplish anything. There are some things you're just going to fail at no matter how hard you try. We all know this intuitively, but it's nice to puncture that platitude.

Was the structure of the play influenced by any other work?

Not particularly. It's quick and simple. It reminds me a bit of Christopher Durang's *Naomi in the Living Room* and Jon Rand's *Drugs are Bad* in that it uses a living room and a family conversation.

Have you dealt with the same theme in other works that you have written?

I think so, honestly. I think that I like to satirize overly saccharine and optimistic things. It just feels like it has more teeth to me, and there are so many positive messages coming to us all the time. I know that's not the prevailing view, but if you follow television and music, you'll find that most of what is being said is pablum. I find it incredibly disturbing that American teenagers rank in the bottom half of the pack worldwide in school performance, but are number one in self-esteem. We've prioritized self-esteem over accomplishment, and that's a theme I've returned to again and again.

What writers have had the most profound effect on your style?
David Lindsay-Abaire and Christopher Durang are some pretty direct influences on this type of play. I also think someone like Oscar Wilde and Jonathan Swift are strong precursors.

What do you hope to achieve with this work?
To give everyone a good laugh, but also to have them recognize that, yes, a lot of what we're told is unrealistic.

What were the biggest challenges involved in the writing of this play?
Trying to square the ending properly. A play like this has to spin, just as soon as the audience gets one joke, you've got to escalate. It's rather tricky, actually.

What are the most common mistakes that occur in productions of your work?
I think people sometime play my work with a wink and nudge at the audience, and that feels wrong to me. I think you have to do any play, even if it's satirical or absurdist, as deadly serious for the characters involved. You must play the reality of the situation, and then the audience will laugh.

What inspired you to become a playwright?
I always wanted to be a writer, but when you're writing novels or short stories, you have to hand off a story and then go away for a while. Then you come back and they lie to you and tell you how much they liked it. With a play, the audience reaction is immediate. It's wonderful (and sometimes horrible) to be able to sit incognito in the audience and actually get a genuine honest reaction to your play. There's nothing like making a room full of people laugh at your joke and have them not know you.

About the Author

Don Zolidis is a former high school and middle school theatre teacher and college professor. Originally hailing from Wisconsin, Mr. Zolidis received his B.A. in English from Carleton College and an MFA in Playwriting from the Actor's Studio Program at the New School. He has received numerous honors, including the 2004 Princess Grace Award for Playwriting for *White Buffalo*, now published by Samuel French. His plays for young people have been produced over 4,300 times in all 50 states and 37 countries and have won numerous state championships. He lives with his wife and his two adorable boys and is hard at work on a novel.

CLOSETED

A short dramedy by
Jonathan Dorf

CAST OF CHARACTERS

ANDREW, early to mid-teens and not the coolest boy in school.

CHLOE, female, same age and way closer to the top of the pecking order.

PRODUCTION NOTE

In two instances, dialogue is followed by [bracketed] text. The bracketed text may substitute for the dialogue it follows if it is more appropriate for your community or production.

ACKNOWLEDGEMENTS

Special thanks to Pam Covington, Billy Houck, Parker Kaeding, Daniel Rashid and Cassidy Shapiro for their assistance in the development of the play.

(A walk-in closet in a home. ANDREW, early to mid-teens, and CHLOE [pronounced Klo-ee], same age, are inside. MUSIC and PARTY SOUNDS come from the other side of the door. The play should begin in almost total darkness, but as the characters' eyes adjust, the light should gradually increase.)

ANDREW: OK, so...

CHLOE: So...

ANDREW: Well, I guess I should come over there. Or...

CHLOE: Or...?

ANDREW: I don't know.

CHLOE: OK...

ANDREW: *(Beat.)* Yeah. I'll come over there. *(Beat as he doesn't move:)* It's weird that in ten minutes, somebody's just gonna open the door. What if they lose count, and ten minutes goes by and you're just waiting? I mean, can you come out on your own, or do you just have to wait? Or what if they open it, but it's only been six minutes? *(Beat.)* Do you think anybody's ever locked the door from the inside?

CHLOE: What are you talking about?

ANDREW: Nothing. I'm just— Nothing.

CHLOE: *(Beat.)* So are you gonna come over?

ANDREW: Do you want me to?

CHLOE: You just said you were. *(Half to herself:)* It's kind of the point.

ANDREW: Where's the light?

CHLOE: You don't turn on the light.

ANDREW: I can't see. I can feel something next to my foot, but I can't see what it is.

CHLOE: Derek's mom has like 75 pairs of shoes.

ANDREW: It doesn't feel like a shoe.

CHLOE: So step over it.

ANDREW: I don't want to break anything.

CHLOE: Haven't you done this before?

ANDREW: Yeah. Of course. But not in this closet.

CHLOE: A closet's a closet.

ANDREW: I mean they usually have like windows and stuff.

CHLOE: Closets don't have windows.

ANDREW: Sometimes they do.

CHLOE: Where?

ANDREW: I don't know.

> *(Beat. Andrew is breathing very deliberately. It's loud.)*

CHLOE: Are you...what do they call it when you breathe really fast?

ANDREW: Hyperventilating. No. *(Beat.)* It's just I used to get panic attacks, and so I have these breathing techniques that keep me from going all...

CHLOE: All...?

ANDREW: My eyes are starting to adjust. I think I can step over it.

> *(He moves toward her, his hand reaching out and feeling the air until he touches her arm.)*

CHLOE: What is that?

ANDREW: That's my hand.

CHLOE: It's all sweaty.

ANDREW: Sorry. It's like really stuffy in here.

CHLOE: So your hand's all sweaty?

ANDREW: *(Beat.)* We don't have to touch hands. *(Beat.)* I just thought— Never mind.

CHLOE: What?

ANDREW: I just thought it would be nice.

CHLOE: That's sweet. *(Beat.)* But sweaty hands just feel kinda gross.

(*Andrew pulls away and blows on his hands.*)

What's that?

ANDREW: Nothing.

CHLOE: I just felt something on my ear.

ANDREW: No.

CHLOE: Are you like blowing on my ear?

ANDREW: I'm trying to dry my hands.

CHLOE: *(As he keeps blowing:)* Stop. You're weirding me out.

ANDREW: Sorry.

CHLOE: There's no point drying them.

ANDREW: I guess.

CHLOE: You're just gonna keep sweating.

ANDREW: Sorry.

CHLOE: It's all right. Let's just not touch hands.

(*Andrew moves away. The sound of a TEXT MESSAGE BEEP.*)

ANDREW: What's that?

CHLOE: None of your business. *(Beat as Chloe checks her phone:)* Janette wants to know if we're making out yet.

ANDREW: Oh. *(Beat.)* What are you gonna tell her? *(Beat.)* Why do they call it Seven Minutes in Heaven if we have ten minutes? *(Beat.)* Sorry. I know you wanted Derek.

CHLOE: Derek's a tool [an idiot].

ANDREW: Isn't he your boyf —

CHLOE: *Ex*-boyfriend.

ANDREW: But you've been holding hands all night.

CHLOE: Cause he doesn't want it to be a whole big thing that we broke up, cause it's his party and he doesn't want the karma or fang shu or whatever to be all messed up, so I said I'd do this one last thing cause of all the good times we had together, which is a total lie, cause we went out for like three months which is totally forever and he bought me one tulip, which I'm like ninety-nine percent sure he stole from the Partridges' garden on his way over, and a stuffed zebra. It's soft, but he knew I wanted a koala and he got me a zebra.

ANDREW: *(Pronounced fung-shway:)* Feng shui.

CHLOE: What?

ANDREW: You said he doesn't want the karma or fang shu to be all messed up. It's feng shui. It's an ancient Chinese science. Well, sort of science with a little magic or mystic thrown in. It means "wind water." It's all about balancing energy in your space so good things happen. So if you want a room to have the right energy, you have to feng shui it by doing stuff like putting plants in the corners to protect against the hard edges, picking the right colors...

CHLOE: Wow. They were right.

ANDREW: Who? Right about what?

CHLOE: Everybody. Everybody says you're like the brain of brains.

ANDREW: I'm not that smart.

CHLOE: You think Mr. Donnelly knows what f...

ANDREW: Feng shui.

CHLOE: *(Carefully parroting him:)* Feng shui is?

ANDREW: Mr. Donnelly is building a school in Kenya next year when he retires.

CHLOE: Doesn't mean he's smart. Just means he's nice.

ANDREW: He designed the building. Even the electrical and sewage systems. I've seen the blueprints.

CHLOE: Total shocker you're never at any of the parties. *(Beat.)* Sorry. That was mean.

ANDREW: It kinda was.

CHLOE: My dad says I better enjoy it now, 'cause when I get older I'm gonna be ugly and stupid and probably poor unless I marry somebody rich. *(Beat.)* I'm really sorry.

ANDREW: *(Beat.)* You'll never be ugly. *(Beat.)* I told Evan I'd do his math for a week if he asked Derek to let me come.

CHLOE: Why would you even want to come here?

ANDREW: Why do you? *(Beat.)* It was either sit at home with my mom practicing for Science Olympiad or...I don't know...

(The sound of a TEXT MESSAGE BEEP. Chloe checks her phone:)

CHLOE: Geez, Janette. She's mad I didn't text her back.

ANDREW: Hey Janette—having an awesome time in the closet with Andrew.

CHLOE: I like it.

ANDREW: What?

CHLOE: I'm texting that.

ANDREW: It was a joke.

CHLOE: It's perfect.

ANDREW: But then she'll know we're not doing anything.

CHLOE: We're not doing anything.

ANDREW: But— Yeah.

CHLOE: And no she won't. Everybody knows I'm the fastest texter in our grade.

(*The sound of a TEXT MESSAGE BEEP. Chloe checks her phone. Reading:*)

OMG.

ANDREW: What?

CHLOE: That's what she texted.

ANDREW: She thinks we're—

CHLOE: She totally thinks we're—

ANDREW: But we're not— And Derek—

CHLOE: Derek can suck it [get over it]. And everybody knows in Seven—

ANDREW: (*Unable to help himself:*) Or Ten—

CHLOE: Minutes in Heaven, boyfriend-girlfriend is automatically suspended.

ANDREW: I did not know that.

CHLOE: We're only fake together anyway.

(*The sound of a TEXT MESSAGE BEEP. Chloe checks her phone:*)

She wants to know if we're regular kissing or French kissing.

ANDREW: What are you telling her?

CHLOE: Regular. 'Cause you're too much of a gentleman on our first time.

(The sound of a TEXT MESSAGE BEEP. Chloe checks her phone.)

OMG, OMG, OMG!

ANDREW: She said OMG three times?

CHLOE: Two. I was the first OMG, but she was the last two and she had one with an exclamation point.

(Chloe texts back.)

ANDREW: Wait.

CHLOE: Too late—I told her you kiss really good.

ANDREW: But—

CHLOE: I told you I'm the fastest texter.

ANDREW: Wait.

CHLOE: We are totally upgrading your rep.

(The sound of a TEXT MESSAGE BEEP.)

ANDREW: Wait. Before you read it.

CHLOE: What?

ANDREW: I don't want to lie about it.

CHLOE: Don't you want to be...like...

ANDREW: What?

CHLOE: People lie about stuff all the time. Everybody thinks me and Derek are totally together, and he never really even liked me and I don't know if I ever liked him either.

ANDREW: *(Beat.)* So why did you do it?

CHLOE: *(Beat.)* People expect stuff.

ANDREW: I don't want to be people. Not that kind.

(The sound of a PHONE BEEPING. Chloe checks her phone:)

CHLOE: That's not mine.

ANDREW: It's our 90-second warning.

CHLOE: You set your alarm? You're kind of freaky.

ANDREW: Anyway, just tell people you were kidding. Tell them my hands were sweaty and I had garlic breath and —

CHLOE: Do you have garlic breath?

ANDREW: No, but —

CHLOE: Who's lying now?

ANDREW: I just don't want people to think we kissed if we didn't. Maybe I'd be upgraded, but I don't want them to think that about you.

CHLOE: Why? I'm not special. I'm not even nice really.

ANDREW: *(Beat.)* I guess we see what we hope to see.

(This strikes a chord in Chloe. A long pause.)

CHLOE: Did you just make that up?

ANDREW: I don't know. I think so.

CHLOE: I think...I think it feels true. *(Beat.)* I don't think I can tell them I lied about the making out. They'd think I lied all the other times.

ANDREW: Did you?

(She kisses him for a long moment. After he gets over his shock, he definitely kisses her back.)

CHLOE: Maybe you can tell me more about what you see sometime.

ANDREW: I'd like that. *(Beat.)* Koala, right?

(The closet door opens as the MUSIC and PARTY SOUNDS get louder. Blackout. End of play.)

The Author Speaks

What inspired you to write this play?
To be honest, we've been wanting to put together a middle school play collection at YouthPLAYS (yes, I'm putting my YouthPLAYS co-founder hat on over top of my author hat, which makes me even taller than usual) for probably close to a year, and I thought we should finally get it done. But I wanted the plays in the collection to be middle school-centric, not merely plays that middle school students could perform but where they mostly had to play much older characters. So while we had a number of plays that were great middle school choices, I wanted to have fifteen of them. That meant finding a few more plays. We went to some of the best writers we knew and asked them to create a piece specifically for performers in this age group, and I thought I should contribute a play as well. Oddly, while I have lots of short plays, they're largely geared toward high school students, so this is probably the first time I said "I'm writing a ten-minute play for middle schoolers." Having said that, the characters' ages are never expressly stated, and I hope that younger high school students will enjoy the play as well.

Was the structure or other elements of the play influenced by any other work?
Most of my ten-minute plays have a similar structure. I like to take two characters, put them in a single space over the course of a single scene, and let them go at it. I love the ten-minute form, as it's a challenge to write a complete play that goes from beginning to end—a complete dramatic thought—in ten minutes. It's sort of the haiku of the playwriting world. Interestingly, many of the scenes in my longer plays are shorter, but for some reason, a ten-minute play that's further fragmented (or moves from place to place) just doesn't feel right to me.

Have you dealt with the same theme in other works that you have written?
My plays are filled with characters who feel as if they're outsiders. In *The Locker Next 2 Mine*, there are a whole series of characters who feel "apart." Alisa is new, and while she may fit in with Brady, neither of them is "inside." Legolas, Habit and Sabrina constitute the most obvious cluster of outsiders, and even Chuck aspires to be a jock and among the popular kids but as hard as he tries—and in some ways it's his undoing—can't cut it in their world. In *Thank You for Flushing My Head in the Toilet and other rarely used expressions*, Achilles and Helen get bullied for not fitting in. And perhaps most "outside" of all is Emmett in *After Math*, who isn't even noticed by the other students at school until he disappears.

What do you hope to achieve with this work?
I don't really like to tell people what they should get out of my plays, because we all have our own responses to pieces of theatre, and that's part of the fun. But having said that, I'm going to write a sentence that could turn out to be completely incomprehensible: sometimes we have more in common with people with whom we think we have nothing in common than we think. We just have to keep an open mind and take that first step toward connection.

What were the biggest challenges involved in the writing of this play?
It's always a challenge to write a play on a deadline, particularly when that deadline is close at hand. I'm lucky that titles tend to come to me, and in this case, the title suggested the set-up (or maybe they came to me together). The challenge, however, was creating the right feel in the writing. I needed the rhythm of the play to create that sense of awkwardness that comes both with the early teen years and with the situation in which our characters find themselves. Also, while

it would make for super cool environmental (i.e. site-specific) theatre if the play could take place in an actual closet, the reality is that most productions won't, and so I needed to consider the realities of what a closet space—both in terms of its physicality and its light—would feel like. Of course, a good director and production team will sort most of that out, but I didn't want to handicap them from the start.

Shakespeare gave advice to the players in *Hamlet*; if you could give advice to your cast what would it be?
Don't be afraid of silence. Young actors in particular tend to want to get to the end as quickly as possible, but fight that urge: much of what's happening in this play is actually happening in the spaces between the lines, so don't rush. If it makes you feel uncomfortable and awkward, great! It's an uncomfortable, awkward situation for the two characters. On that note, pay attention to the punctuation—I spend a lot of time on punctuation as I try to find the right rhythm, so every mark is there for a reason. Also, yes, some of the issues Andrew and Chloe are dealing with are serious, but don't try to play them as "serious" or "important"—in fact, don't forget that there's (I hope) plenty of humor here too. So have fun. Enjoy the release of being someone who is not you for a little while.

About the Author

Jonathan Dorf is a Los Angeles-based playwright, screenwriter, teacher and script consultant, whose plays have been produced in every state in the US, as well as in Canada, Europe, Asia, Africa, South America, Australia and New Zealand. He is Co-Chair of the Alliance of Los Angeles Playwrights and the Resident Playwriting Expert for Final Draft and The Writers Store. He directed the theatre program at The Haverford School and spent three years at Choate

Rosemary Hall Summer Arts Conservatory as playwright-in-residence. A frequent guest artist at Thespian conferences and schools, he has served as Visiting Professor of Theatre in the MFA Playwriting and Children's Literature programs at Hollins University, and as United States cultural envoy to Barbados. He holds a BA in Dramatic Writing and Literature from Harvard College and an MFA in Playwriting from UCLA. He is a member of The Dramatists Guild.

About YouthPLAYS

YouthPLAYS (www.youthplays.com) is a publisher of award-winning professional dramatists and talented new discoveries, each with an original theatrical voice, and all dedicated to expanding the vocabulary of theatre for young actors and audiences. On our website you'll find one-act and full-length plays and musicals for teen and pre-teen (and even college) actors, as well as duets and monologues for competition. Many of our authors' works have been widely produced at high schools and middle schools, youth theatres and other TYA companies, both amateur and professional, as well as at elementary schools, camps, churches and other institutions serving young audiences and/or actors worldwide. Most are intended for performance by young people, while some are intended for adult actors performing for young audiences.

YouthPLAYS was co-founded by professional playwrights Jonathan Dorf and Ed Shockley. It began merely as an additional outlet to market their own works, which included a substantial body of award-winning published and unpublished plays and musicals. Those interested in their published plays were directed to the respective publishers' websites, and unpublished plays were made available in electronic form. But when they saw the desperate need for material for young actors and audiences—coupled with their experience that numerous quality plays for young people weren't finding a home—they made the decision to represent the work of other playwrights as well. Dozens and dozens of authors are now members of the YouthPLAYS family, with scripts available both electronically and in traditional acting editions. We continue to grow as we look for exciting and challenging plays and musicals for young actors and audiences.

About ProduceaPlay.com

Let's put up a play! Great idea! But producing a play takes time, energy and knowledge. While finding the necessary time and energy is up to you, ProduceaPlay.com is a website designed to assist you with that third element: knowledge.

Created by YouthPLAYS' co-founders, Jonathan Dorf and Ed Shockley, ProduceaPlay.com serves as a resource for producers at all levels as it addresses the many facets of production. As Dorf and Shockley speak from their years of experience (as playwrights, producers, directors and more), they are joined by a group of award-winning theatre professionals and experienced teachers from the world of academic theatre, all making their expertise available for free in the hope of helping this and future generations of producers, whether it's at the school or university level, or in community or professional theatres.

The site is organized into a series of major topics, each of which has its own page that delves into the subject in detail, offering suggestions and links for further information. For example, Publicity covers everything from Publicizing Auditions to How to Use Social Media to Posters to whether it's worth hiring a publicist. Casting details Where to Find the Actors, How to Evaluate a Resume, Callbacks and even Dealing with Problem Actors. You'll find guidance on your Production Timeline, The Theater Space, Picking a Play, Budget, Contracts, Rehearsing the Play, The Program, House Management, Backstage, and many other important subjects.

The site is constantly under construction, so visit often for the latest insights on play producing, and let it help make your play production dreams a reality.

More from YouthPLAYS

Dear Chuck by Jonathan Dorf
Dramedy. 80-90 minutes. 8-50+ performers (gender flexible).

Teenagers are caught in the middle—they're not quite adults, but they're definitely no longer children. Through scenes and monologues, we meet an eclectic group of teens trying to communicate with that wannabe special someone, coping with the loss of a classmate, battling controlling parents, swimming for that island of calm in the stormy sea of technology—and many others. What they all have in common is the search for their "Chuck," that elusive moment of knowing who you are. Also available in a one-act version.

The Old New Kid by Adam J. Goldberg
Comedy. 30-40 minutes. 3-10+ females, 2-9+ males (8-30+ performers possible).

It's the half-day of school before Thanksgiving break, and current "new kid" Alan Socrates Bama just wants to get through the day. But when a new-new kid arrives, things change. Alan has three hours to find the meaning of Thanksgiving, survive elementary school politics, battle for his identity, and spell the word "cornucopia" in this *Peanuts*-flavored comedy for kids of all ages.

Herby Alice Counts Down to Yesterday by Nicole B. Adkins
Comedy. 30-35 minutes. 3 females, 3 males, 4-20+ either (10-50+ performers possible).

Middle school rocket scientist Herby Alice has ambitions as big as the universe, and no time for interviews. Rose Plum, media hopeful, needs a juicy story to get in good with the school broadcast elite. How far is she willing to go to be a star? Or will mad scientists, aliens, befuddled teachers, demanding executives, and the space-time continuum overrun the show?

ShakeSPLOSION!!! by Andrew Geha
Comedy. 75-85 minutes. 9-21+ females, 4-14+ males (14-100+ performers possible).

ShakeSPLOSION!!! is a madcap sprint through every play written by the Bard. From 235 years of English kings in the History Plays, to (nearly) every bloody death in the Tragedies, to every girl who dressed up as a boy in the Comedies, it's like watching Shakespeare's entire canon fired out of a cannon—scattering prose, verse and characters across the stage. Sword fights! Word fights! Witches, ghosts and murder! All in 80 minutes!! Performed by teenagers!!!

Camp Monster by Sharyn Rothstein (book and lyrics) and Kris Kukul (music)
Musical. 60-75 minutes. 8-11 females, 7-11 males (15-22 performers possible).

For years, the sons and daughters of the world's most famous monsters have spent their summers at Camp Flonster, the only camp where young monsters can be themselves. But this year, Camp Flonster has a new director, the oppressive and diabolical Roseanne Finicula, who harbors a secret desire to rid the world of all monsters! When the young monsters learn of Roseanne's plot, they must put aside their daily squabbles to work together and beat her at her own game—and keep the world safe for even the strangest among us.

The Superhero Ultraferno by Don Zolidis
Comedy. 30-40 minutes. 6-20 females, 6-20 males (12-50+ performers).

Now that nerds have taken over the world, it's imperative that all popular kids learn everything they can about comic book superheroes. Join two nerds and a crack team of actors as they race hilariously through the world of tights-wearing crimefighters, from the 1960s TV Batman to the soap opera insanity of the Fantastic Four to a bizarre, German opera of Spiderman. Also available as a full-length.

Made in the USA
Lexington, KY
26 October 2018